RICE

The World's Classics

CCCCXLIX
A CHRISTMAS
GARLAND
By MAX BEERBOHM

A CHRISTMAS GARLAND *woven*

by MAX BEERBOHM

The World's
Classics

NEW YORK
OXFORD UNIVERSITY PRESS

Reprinted by permission of E. P. Dutton & Co. Inc.,
New York

First Printing October 1936
Reprinted January 1937

PRINTED IN THE UNITED STATES OF AMERICA

NOTE

Stevenson, in one of his essays, tells us how he "played the sedulous ape" to Hazlitt, Sir Thomas Browne, Montaigne, and other writers of the past. And the compositors of all our higher-toned newspapers keep the foregoing sentence set up in type always, so constantly does it come tripping off the pens of all higher-toned reviewers. Nor ever do I read it without a fresh thrill of respect for the young Stevenson. I, in my own very inferior boyhood, found it hard to revel in so much as a single page of any writer earlier than Thackeray. This disability I did not shake off, alas, after I left school. There seemed to be so many live authors worth reading. I gave precedence to them, and, not being much of a reader, never had time to grapple with the old masters. Meanwhile, I was already writing a little on my own account. I had had some sort of aptitude for Latin prose and Latin verse. I wondered often whether those two things, essential though they were (and are) to the making of a decent style in English prose, sufficed for the making of a style more than decent. I felt that I must have other models. And thus I acquired the habit of aping, now and again, quite sedulously, this or that live writer — sometimes, it must be admitted, in the hope of learning rather what to avoid. I acquired, too, the habit of publishing these patient little efforts. Some of them appeared in "The Saturday Review" many years ago; others appeared there more recently. I have selected, by kind permission of the Editor, one from the earlier lot, and seven from the later. The other nine in this book are printed for the first time. The book itself may be taken as a sign that I think my own style is, at length, more or less formed.

M. B.

Rapallo, 1912.

CONTENTS

THE MOTE IN THE MIDDLE DISTANCE

By

H*NRY J*M*S

THE MOTE IN THE MIDDLE DISTANCE

IT was with the sense of a, for him, very memorable something that he peered now into the immediate future, and tried, not without compunction, to take that period up where he had, prospectively, left it. But just where the deuce *had* he left it? The consciousness of dubiety was, for our friend, not, this morning, quite yet clean-cut enough to outline the figures on what she had called his "horizon," between which and himself the twilight was indeed of a quality somewhat intimidating. He had run up, in the course of time, against a good number of "teasers"; and the function of teasing them back — of, as it were, giving them, every now and then, "what for"— was in him so much a habit that he would have been at a loss had there been, on the face of it, nothing to lose. Oh, he always had offered rewards, of course — had ever so liberally pasted the windows of his soul with staring appeals, minute descriptions, promises that knew no bounds. But the actual recovery of the article — the business of drawing and crossing the cheque, blotched though this were with tears of joy — had blankly appeared to him rather in the light of a sacrilege, casting, he sometimes felt, a palpable chill on the fervour of the next quest. It was just this fervour that was threatened as, raising himself on his elbow, he stared at the foot of his bed. That his eyes refused to rest there for more than the fraction of an instant, may be taken — *was*, even then, taken by Keith Tantalus — as a hint of his recollection that after all the phenomenon wasn't to be singular. Thus the exact repetition, at the foot of Eva's bed, of the shape pendulous at the foot of *his* was hardly enough to account for the fixity with which he envisaged it, and for which he was to find, some years later, a motive in the (as it turned out) hardly generous fear that Eva had already made the great investigation "on her own." Her very regular breathing presently reassured him that, if she *had* peeped into "her" stocking, she must have done so in sleep. Whether he should wake her now, or wait for their nurse to wake them both in due course, was a problem presently solved

[4]

by a new development. It was plain that his sister was now watching him between her eyelashes. He had half expected that. She really was — he had often told her that she really was — magnificent; and her magnificence was never more obvious than in the pause that elapsed before she all of a sudden remarked "They so very indubitably *are,* you know !"

It occurred to him as befitting Eva's remoteness, which was a part of Eva's magnificence, that her voice emerged somewhat muffled by the bedclothes. She was ever, indeed, the most telephonic of her sex. In talking to Eva you always had, as it were, your lips to the receiver. If you didn't try to meet her fine eyes, it was that you simply couldn't hope to : there were too many dark, too many buzzing and bewildering and all frankly not negotiable leagues in between. Snatches of other voices seemed often to intertrude themselves in the parley ; and your loyal effort not to overhear these was complicated by your fear of missing what Eva might be twittering. "Oh, you certainly haven't, my dear, the trick of propinquity !" was a thrust she had once parried by saying

that, in that case, *he* hadn't — to which his
unspoken rejoinder that she had caught her
tone from the peevish young women at the
Central seemed to him (if not perhaps in the
last, certainly in the last but one, analysis) to
lack finality. With Eva, he had found, it
was always safest to "ring off." It was with
a certain sense of his rashness in the matter,
therefore, that he now, with an air of fever-
ishly "holding the line," said "Oh, as to
that !"

Had *she,* he presently asked himself, "rung
off" ? It was characteristic of our friend —
was indeed "him all over" — that his fear of
what she was going to say was as nothing to
his fear of what she might be going to leave
unsaid. He had, in his converse with her,
been never so conscious as now of the inter-
vening leagues ; they had never so insistently
beaten the drum of his ear ; and he caught
himself in the act of awfully computing, with
a certain statistical passion, the distance between Rome and Boston. He has never been
able to decide which of these points he was
psychically the nearer to at the moment when
Eva, replying "Well, one does, anyhow, leave
a margin for the pretext, you know !" made

[6]

him, for the first time in his life, wonder whether she were not more magnificent than even he had ever given her credit for being. Perhaps it was to test this theory, or perhaps merely to gain time, that he now raised himself to his knees, and, leaning with outstretched arm towards the foot of his bed, made as though to touch the stocking which Santa Claus had, overnight, left dangling there. His posture, as he stared obliquely at Eva, with a sort of beaming defiance, recalled to him something seen in an "illustration." This reminiscence, however — if such it was, save in the scarred, the poor dear old woebegone and so very beguilingly *not* refractive mirror of the moment — took a peculiar twist from Eva's behaviour. She had, with startling suddenness, sat bolt upright, and looked to him as if she were overhearing some tragedy at the other end of the wire, where, in the nature of things, she was unable to arrest it. The gaze she fixed on her extravagant kinsman was of a kind to make him wonder how he contrived to remain, as he beautifully did, rigid. His prop was possibly the reflection that flashed on him that, if *she* abounded in attenuations, well, hang

[7]

it all, so did *he!* It was simply a difference of plane. Readjust the "values," as painters say, and there you were! He was to feel that he was only too crudely "there" when, leaning further forward, he laid a chubby forefinger on the stocking, causing that receptacle to rock ponderously to and fro. This effect was more expected than the tears which started to Eva's eyes, and the intensity with which "Don't you," she exclaimed, "see?"

"The mote in the middle distance?" he asked. "Did you ever, my dear, know me to see anything else? I tell you it blocks out everything. It's a cathedral, it's a herd of elephants, it's the whole habitable globe. Oh, it's, believe me, of an obsessiveness!" But his sense of the one thing it *didn't* block out from his purview enabled him to launch at Eva a speculation as to just how far Santa Claus had, for the particular occasion, gone. The gauge, for both of them, of this seasonable distance seemed almost blatantly suspended in the silhouettes of the two stockings. Over and above the basis of (presumably) sweetmeats in the toes and heels, certain extrusions stood for a very plenary fulfilment of desire. And, since Eva *had* set her heart on a doll of ample proportions and practicable eyelids — *had* asked that most admirable of her sex, their mother, for it with not less directness than he himself had put into his demand for a sword and helmet — her coyness now struck Keith as lying near to, at indeed a hardly measurable distance from, the border-line of his patience. If she didn't *want* the doll, why the deuce had she made such a point of getting it? He was perhaps on the verge of putting this question to her, when, waving her hand to include both stockings, she said "Of course, my dear, you *do* see. There they are, and you know I know you know we wouldn't, either of us, dip a finger into them." With a vibrancy of tone that seemed to bring her voice quite close to him, "One doesn't," she added, "violate the shrine — pick the pearl from the shell!"

Even had the answering question "Doesn't one just?" which for an instant hovered on the tip of his tongue, been uttered, it could not have obscured for Keith the change which her magnificence had wrought in him. Something, perhaps, of the bigotry of the convert was already discernible in the way that, averting his eyes, he said "One doesn't even peer." As to whether, in the years that have elapsed since he said this either of our friends (now adult) has, in fact, "peered," is a question which, whenever I call at the house, I am tempted to put to one or other of them. But any regret I may feel in my invariable failure to "come up to the scratch" of yielding to this temptation is balanced, for me, by my impression — my sometimes all but throned and anointed certainty — that the answer, if vouchsafed, would be in the negative.

P.C., X, 36

By

R*D**RD K*PL*NG

Then it's collar 'im tight,
  In the name o' the Lawd !
'Ustle 'im, shake 'im till 'e's sick !
  Wot, 'e *would*, would 'e ? Well,
  Then yer've got ter give 'im 'Ell,
An' it's trunch, trunch, truncheon does the trick.
                    POLICE STATION DITTIES.

I HAD spent Christmas Eve at the Club, listening to a grand pow-wow between certain of the choicer sons of Adam. Then Slushby had cut in. Slushby is one who writes to newspapers and is theirs obediently "HUMANITARIAN." When Slushby cuts in, men remember they have to be up early next morning.

Sharp round a corner on the way home, I collided with something firmer than the regulation pillar-box. I righted myself after the recoil and saw some stars that were very pretty indeed. Then I perceived the nature of the obstruction.

"Evening, Judlip," I said sweetly, when I

had collected my hat from the gutter. "Have I broken the law, Judlip? If so, I'll go quiet."

"Time yer was in bed," grunted X, 36. "Yer Ma'll be lookin' out for yer."

This from the friend of my bosom! It hurt. Many were the night-beats I had been privileged to walk with Judlip, imbibing curious lore that made glad the civilian heart of me. Seven whole 8 x 5 inch note-books had I pitmanised to the brim with Judlip. And now to be repulsed as one of the un-initiated! It hurt horrid.

There is a thing called Dignity. Small boys sometimes stand on it. Then they have to be kicked. Then they get down, weeping. I don't stand on Dignity.

"What's wrong, Judlip?" I asked, more sweetly than ever. "Drawn a blank to-night?"

"Yuss. Drawn a blank blank blank. 'Aven't 'ad so much as a kick at a lorst dorg. Christmas Eve ain't wot it was." I felt for my note-book. "Lawd! I remembers the time when the drunks and disorderlies down this street was as thick as flies on a fly-paper. One just picked 'em orf with one's finger and thumb. A bloomin' battew, that's wot it wos."

"The night's yet young, Judlip," I insinuated, with a jerk of my thumb at the flaring windows of the "Rat and Blood Hound." At that moment the saloon-door swung open, emitting a man and woman who walked with linked arms and exceeding great care.

Judlip eyed them longingly as they tacked up the street. Then he sighed. Now, when Judlip sighs the sound is like unto that which issues from the vent of a Crosby boiler when the cog-gauges are at 260° F.

"Come, Judlip!" I said. "Possess your soul in patience. You'll soon find someone to make an example of. Meanwhile"— I threw back my head and smacked my lips —"the usual, Judlip?"

In another minute I emerged through the swing-door, bearing a furtive glass of that same "usual," and nipped down the mews where my friend was wont to await these little tokens of esteem.

"To the Majesty of the Law, Judlip!"

When he had honoured the toast, I scooted back with the glass, leaving him wiping the beads off his beard-bristles. He was in his

[15]

philosophic mood when I rejoined him at the corner.

"Wot am I ?" he said, as we paced along. "A bloomin' cypher. Wot's the sarjint ? 'E's got the Inspector over 'im. Over above the Inspector there's the Sooprintendent. Over above 'im's the old red-tape-masticatin' Yard. Over above that there's the 'Ome Sec. Wot's 'e ? A cypher, like me. Why ?" Judlip looked up at the stars. "Over above 'im's We Dunno Wot. Somethin' wot issues its horders an' regulations an' divisional injunctions, inscrootable like, but p'remptory ; an' we 'as ter see as 'ow they're carried out, not arskin' no questions, but each man goin' about 'is dooty."

"'Is dooty,'" said I, looking up from my note-book. "Yes, I've got that."

"Life ain't a bean-feast. It's a 'arsh reality. An' them as makes it a bean-feast 'as got to be 'arshly dealt with accordin'. That's wot the Force is put 'ere for from Above. Not as 'ow we ain't fallible. We makes our mistakes. An' when we makes 'em we sticks to 'em. For the honour o' the Force. Which same is the jool Britannia wears on 'er bosom as a charm against hanarchy. That's wot the brarsted old Beaks don't understand. Yer remember Smithers of our Div ?"

I remembered Smithers — well. As fine, up-standing, square-toed, bullet-headed, clean-living a son of a gun as ever perjured himself in the box. There was nothing of the softy about Smithers. I took off my billicock to Smithers' memory.

"Sacrificed to public opinion ? Yuss," said Judlip, pausing at a front door and flashing his 45 c.p. down the slot of a two-grade Yale. "Sacrificed to a parcel of screamin' old women wot ort ter 'ave gorn down on their knees an' thanked Gawd for such a protector. 'E'll be out in another 'alf year. Wot'll 'e do then, pore devil ? Go a bust on 'is con-duc' money an' throw in 'is lot with them same hexperts wot 'ad a 'oly terror of 'im." Then Judlip swore gently.

"What should you do, O Great One, if ever it were your duty to apprehend him ?"

"Do ? Why, yer blessed innocent, yer don't think I'd shirk a fair clean cop ? Same time, I don't say as 'ow I wouldn't 'andle 'im tender like, for sake o' wot 'e wos. Likewise 'cos 'e'd be a stiff customer to tackle. Like-wise 'cos——"

[17]

He had broken off, and was peering fixedly upwards at an angle of 85° across the moonlit street. "'Ullo!" he said in a hoarse whisper.

Striking an average between the direction of his eyes—for Judlip, when on the job, has a soul-stirring squint—I perceived someone in the act of emerging from a chimney-pot.

Judlip's voice clove the silence. "Wot are yer doin' hup there?"

The person addressed came to the edge of the parapet. I saw then that he had a hoary white beard, a red ulster with the hood up, and what looked like a sack over his shoulder. He said something or other in a voice like a concertina that has been left out in the rain.

"I dessay," answered my friend. "Just you come down, an' we'll see about that."

The old man nodded and smiled. Then —as I hope to be saved— he came floating gently down through the moonlight, with the sack over his shoulder and a young fir-tree clasped to his chest. He alighted in a friendly manner on the curb beside us.

Judlip was the first to recover himself. Out went his right arm, and the airman was slung round by the scruff of the neck, spilling his sack in the road. I made a bee-line for his shoulder-blades. Burglar or no burglar, he was the best airman out, and I was muchly desirous to know the precise nature of the apparatus under his ulster. A backhander from Judlip's left caused me to hop quickly aside. The prisoner was squealing and whimpering. He didn't like the feel of Judlip's knuckles at his cervical vertebræ.

"Wot wos yer doin' hup there ?" asked Judlip, tightening the grip.

"I'm S-Santa Claus, Sir. P-please, Sir, let me g-go."

"Hold him," I shouted. "He's a German."

"It's my dooty ter caution yer that wotever yer say now may be used in hevidence against yer, yer old sinner. Pick up that there sack, an' come along o' me."

The captive snivelled something about peace on earth, good will toward men.

"Yuss," said Judlip. "That's in the Noo Testament, ain't it ? The Noo Testament contains some uncommon nice readin' for old gents an' young ladies. But it ain't included in the librery o' the Force. We confine ourselves to the Old Testament—O.T., 'ot. An' 'ot you'll get it. Hup with that sack, an' quick march !"

I have seen worse attempts at a neck-wrench, but it was just not slippery enough for Judlip. And the kick that Judlip then let fly was a thing of beauty and a joy for ever.

"Frog's-march him !" I shrieked, dancing. "For the love of heaven, frog's-march him !"

Trotting by Judlip's side to the Station, I reckoned it out that if Slushby had not been at the Club I should not have been here to see. Which shows that even Slushbys are put into this world for a purpose.

OUT OF HARM'S WAY

By

A. C. B*NS*N

OUT OF HARM'S WAY

Chapter XLII. — Christmas

MORE and more, as the tranquil years went by, Percy found himself able to draw a quiet satisfaction from the regularity, the even sureness, with which, in every year, one season succeeded to another. In boyhood he had felt always a little sad at the approach of autumn. The yellowing leaves of the lime trees, the creeper that flushed to so deep a crimson against the old grey walls, the chrysanthemums that shed so prodigally their petals on the smooth green lawn — all these things, beautiful and wonderful though they were, were somehow a little melancholy also, as being signs of the year's decay. Once, when he was fourteen or fifteen years old, he had overheard a friend of the family say to his father "How the days are drawing in !" — a remark which set him thinking deeply, with an almost morbid abandonment to gloom, for quite a long time. He had not then grasped the truth that in exactly the proportion in which the days draw in they will, in the fullness of time, draw out. This was a lesson that he mastered in later years. And, though the waning of summer never failed to touch him with the sense of an almost personal loss, yet it seemed to him a right thing, a wise ordination, that there should be these recurring changes. Those men and women of whom the poet tells us that they lived in "a land where it was always afternoon" — could they, Percy often wondered, have felt quite that thankfulness which on a fine afternoon is felt by us dwellers in ordinary climes ? Ah, no ! Surely it is because we are made acquainted with the grey sadness of twilight, the solemn majesty of the night-time, the faint chill of the dawn, that we set so high a value on the more meridional hours. If there were no autumn, no winter, then spring and summer would lose, not all indeed, yet an appreciable part of their sweet savour for us. Thus, as his mind matured, Percy came to be very glad of the gradual changes of the year. He found in them *a rhythm,* as he once described it in his diary ; and this he liked very much indeed. He was aware that in his own character, with its tendency to waywardness, to caprice, to disorder, there was an almost grievous lack of this *rhythmic* quality. In the sure and seemly progression of the months, was there not for him a desirable exemplar, a needed corrective ? He was so liable to moods in which he rebelled against the performance of some quite simple duty, some appointed task — moods in which he said to himself "H-ng it ! I will not do this," or "Oh, b-th-r ! I shall not do that !" But it was clear that Nature herself never spoke thus. Even as a passenger in a frail barque on the troublous ocean will keep his eyes directed towards some upstanding rock on the far horizon, finding thus inwardly for himself, or hoping to find, a more stable equilibrium, a deeper tranquillity, than is his, so did Percy daily devote a certain portion of his time to quiet communion with the almanac.

There were times when he was sorely tempted to regret a little that some of the feasts of the Church were "moveable." True, they moved only within strictly prescribed limits, and in accordance with certain unalterable, wholly justifiable rules. Yet, in the

very fact that they did move, there seemed
— to use an expressive slang phrase of the
day — "something not quite nice." It was
therefore the fixed feasts that pleased Percy
best, and on Christmas Day, especially, he
experienced a temperate glow which would
have perhaps surprised those who knew him
only slightly.

By reason of the athletic exercises of his
earlier years, Percy had retained in middle
life a certain lightness and firmness of tread ;
and this on Christmas morning, between his
rooms and the Cathedral, was always so
peculiarly elastic that he might almost have
seemed to be rather running than walking.
The ancient fane, with its soarings of grey
columns to the dimness of its embowed roof,
the delicate traceries of the organ screen, the
swelling notes of the organ, the mellow shafts
of light filtered through the stained-glass
windows whose hues were as those of emer-
alds and rubies and amethysts, the stainless
purity of the surplices of clergy and choir,
the sober richness of Sunday bonnets in the
transept, the faint yet heavy fragrance exhaled
from the hot-water pipes — all these familiar
things, appealing, as he sometimes felt, almost

too strongly to that sensuous side of his nature which made him so susceptible to the paintings of Mr. Leader, of Sir Luke Fildes, were on Christmas morning more than usually affecting by reason of that note of quiet joyousness, of peace and good will, that pervaded the lessons of the day, the collect, the hymns, the sermon.

It was this spiritual aspect of Christmas that Percy felt to be hardly sufficiently regarded, or at least dwelt on, nowadays, and he sometimes wondered whether the modern Christmas had not been in some degree inspired and informed by Charles Dickens. He had for that writer a very sincere admiration, though he was inclined to think that his true excellence lay not so much in faithful portrayal of the life of his times, or in gift of sustained narration, or in those scenes of pathos which have moved so many hearts in so many quiet homes, as in the power of inventing highly fantastic figures, such as Mr. Micawber or Mr. Pickwick. This view Percy knew to be somewhat heretical, and, constitutionally averse from the danger of being suspected of "talking for effect," he kept it to himself; but, had anyone chal-

lenged him to give his opinion, it was thus
that he would have expressed himself. In
regard to Christmas, he could not help wishing that Charles Dickens had laid more stress
on its spiritual element. It was right that
the feast should be an occasion for good
cheer, for the savoury meats, the steaming
bowl, the blazing log, the traditional games.
But was not the modern world, with its
almost avowed bias towards materialism, too
little apt to think of Christmas as also a time
for meditation, for taking stock, as it were,
of the things of the soul? Percy had heard
that in London nowadays there was a class
of people who sate down to their Christmas
dinners in public hotels. He did not con-
demn this practice. He never condemned a
thing, but wondered, rather, whether it were
right, and could not help feeling that somehow it was not. In the course of his rare
visits to London he had more than once been
inside of one of the large new hotels that had
sprung up—these "great caravanseries," as
he described them in a letter to an old school-
fellow who had been engaged for many years
in Chinese mission work. And it seemed to
him that the true spirit of Christmas could

hardly be acclimatised in such places, but found its proper resting-place in quiet, detached homes, where were gathered together only those connected with one another by ties of kinship, or of long and tested friendship.

He sometimes blamed himself for having tended more and more, as the quiet, peaceful, tranquil years went by, to absent himself from even those small domestic gatherings. And yet, might it not be that his instinct for solitude at this season was a right instinct, at least for him, and that to run counter to it would be in some degree unacceptable to the Power that fashioned us ? Thus he allowed himself to go, as it were, his own way. After morning service, he sate down to his Christmas fare alone, and then, when the simple meal was over, would sit and think in his accustomed chair, falling perhaps into one of those quiet dozes from which, because they seemed to be so natural a result, so seemly a consummation, of his thoughts, he did not regularly abstain. Later, he sallied forth, with a sense of refreshment, for a brisk walk among the fens, the sedges, the hedgerows, the reed-fringed pools, the pollard willows that would in due course be putting forth their tender shoots of palest green. And then, once more in his rooms, with the curtains drawn and the candles lit, he would turn to his book-shelves and choose from among them some old book that he knew and loved, or maybe some quite new book by that writer whose works were most dear to him because in them he seemed always to know so precisely what the author would say next, and because he found in their finespun repetitions a singular repose, a sense of security, an earnest of calm and continuity, as though he were reading over again one of those wise copy-books that he had so loved in boyhood, or were listening to the sounds made on a piano by some modest, very conscientious young girl with a pale red pig-tail, practising her scales, very gently, hour after hour, next door.

PERKINS AND
MANKIND
By
H. G. W*LLS

PERKINS AND MANKIND

Chapter XX

§ 1

IT was the Christmas party at Heighton that was one of the turning-points in Perkins' life. The Duchess had sent him a three-page wire in the hyperbolical style of her class, conveying a vague impression that she and the Duke had arranged to commit suicide together if Perkins didn't "chuck" any previous engagement he had made. And Perkins had felt in a slipshod sort of way — for at this period he was incapable of ordered thought — he might as well be at Heighton as anywhere . . . .

The enormous house was almost full. There must have been upwards of fifty people sitting down to every meal. Many of these were members of the family. Perkins was able to recognise them by their unconvoluted ears — the well-known Grifford ear, transmitted from one generation to another. For the rest there were the usual lot from the Front Benches and the Embassies. Evesham was there, clutching at the lapels of his coat; and the Prescotts — he with his massive mask of a face, and she with her quick, hawk-like ways, talking about two things at a time; old Tommy Strickland, with his monocle and his dropped g's, telling you what he had once said to Mr. Disraeli; Boubou Seaforth and his American wife; John Pirram, ardent and elegant, spouting old French lyrics; and a score of others.

Perkins had got used to them by now. He no longer wondered what they were "up to," for he knew they were up to nothing whatever. He reflected, while he was dressing for dinner on Christmas night, how odd it was he had ever thought of Using them. He might as well have hoped to Use the Dresden shepherds and shepherdesses that grinned out in the last stages of refinement at him from the glazed cabinets in the drawing-rooms . . . . Or the Labour Members themselves . . . .

True there was Evesham. He had shown an exquisitely open mind about the whole thing. He had at once grasped the underlying principles, thrown out some amazingly luminous suggestions. Oh yes, Evesham was a statesman, right enough. But had even he ever really *believed* in the idea of a Provisional Government of England by the Female Foundlings ?

To Perkins the whole thing had seemed so simple, so imminent — a thing that needed only a little general good-will to bring it about. And now . . . Suppose his Bill *had* passed its Second Reading, suppose it had become Law, would this poor old England be by way of functioning decently — after all ? Foundlings were sometimes naughty. . . .

What was the matter with the whole human race ? He remembered again those words of Scragson's that had had such a depressing effect on him at the Cambridge Union — "Look here, you know ! It's all a huge nasty mess, and we're trying to swab it up with a pocket handkerchief." Well, he'd given up trying to do that. . . .

§ 2

During dinner his eyes wandered furtively up and down the endless ornate table, and he felt he had been, in a sort of way, right

[35]

in thinking these people were the handiest instrument to prise open the national conscience with. The shining red faces of the men, the shining white necks and arms of the women, the fearless eyes, the general free-and-easiness and spaciousness, the look of late hours counteracted by fresh air and exercise and the best things to eat and drink — what mightn't be made of these people, if they'd only Submit ?

Perkins looked behind them, at the solemn young footmen passing and repassing, noiselessly, in blue and white liveries. *They* had Submitted. And it was just because they had been able to that they were no good.

"Damn !" said Perkins, under his breath.

§ 3

One of the big conifers from the park had been erected in the hall, and this, after dinner, was found to be all lighted up with electric bulbs and hung with packages in tissue paper.

The Duchess stood, a bright, feral figure, distributing these packages to the guests. Perkins' name was called out in due course and the package addressed to him was slipped into his hand. He retired with it into a corner. Inside the tissue-paper was a small morocco leather case. Inside that was a set of diamond and sapphire sleeve-links — large ones.

He stood looking at them, blinking a little.

He supposed he must put them on. But something in him, some intractably tough bit of his old self, rose up protesting — frantically.

If he couldn't Use these people, at least they weren't going to Use *him!*

"No, damn it!" he said under his breath, and, thrusting the case into his pocket, slipped away unobserved.

§ 4

He flung himself into a chair in his bedroom and puffed a blast of air from his lungs. . . . Yes, it had been a narrow escape. He knew that if he had put those beastly blue and white things on he would have been a lost soul. . . .

"You've got to pull yourself together, d'you hear?" he said to himself. "You've got to do a lot of clear, steady, merciless thinking — now, to-night. You've got to persuade yourself somehow that, Foundlings or no Foundlings, this regeneration of mankind business may still be set going — and by *you*."

He paced up and down the room, fuming. How recapture the generous certitudes that had one by one been slipping away from him ? He found himself staring vacantly at the row of books on the little shelf by his bed. One of them seemed suddenly to detach itself — he could almost have sworn afterwards that he didn't reach out for it, but that it hopped down into his hand. . . .

"Sitting Up For The Dawn" ! It was one of that sociological series by which H. G. W*lls had first touched his soul to finer issues when he was at the 'Varsity.

He opened it with tremulous fingers. Could it re-exert its old sway over him now ?

The page he had opened it at was headed "General Cessation Day," and he began to read. . . .

"The re-casting of the calendar on a decimal basis seems a simple enough matter at first sight. But even here there are details that will have to be thrashed out. . . .

"Mr. Edgar Dibbs, in his able pamphlet

'Ten to the Rescue,'[1] advocates a twenty-hour day, and has drawn up an ingenious scheme for accelerating the motion of this planet by four in every twenty-four hours, so that the alternations of light and darkness shall be re-adjusted to the new reckoning. I think such re-adjustment would be indispensable (though I know there is a formidable body of opinion against me). But I am far from being convinced of the feasibility of Mr. Dibbs' scheme. I believe the twenty-four hour day has come to stay — anomalous though it certainly will seem in the ten-day week, the fifty-day month, and the thousand-day year. I should like to have incorporated Mr. Dibbs' scheme in my vision of the Dawn. But, as I have said, the scope of this vision is purely practical. . . .

"Mr. Albert Baker, in a paper[2] read before the South Brixton Hebdomadals, pleads that the first seven days of the decimal week should retain their old names, the other three to be called provisionally Huxleyday, Marxday, and Tolstoiday. But, for reasons which

[1] Published by the Young Self-Helpers' Press, Ipswich.
[2] "Are We Going Too Fast?"

[39]

I have set forth elsewhere,[1] I believe that the
nomenclature which I had originally suggested [2] —Aday, Bday, and so on to Jday—
would be really the simplest way out of the
difficulty. Any fanciful way of naming the
days would be bad, as too sharply differen-
tiating one day from another. What we
must strive for in the Dawn is that every day
shall be as nearly as possible like every other
day. We must help the human units—
these little pink slobbering creatures of the
Future whose cradle we are rocking—to
progress not in harsh jerks, but with a beautiful unconscious rhythm. . . .

"There must be nothing corresponding to
our Sunday. Sunday is a canker that must
be cut ruthlessly out of the social organism.
At present the whole community gets 'slack'
on Saturday because of the paralysis that is
about to fall on it. And then 'Black Mon-
day' ! — that day when the human brain tries
to readjust itself — tries to realise that the
shutters are down, and the streets are swept,

[1] "A Midwife For The Millennium." H. G.
W✳lls.
[2] How To Be Happy Though Yet Unborn." H. G.
W✳lls.

and the stove-pipe hats are back in their band-boxes. . . .

"Yet of course there must be holidays. We can no more do without holidays than without sleep. For every man there must be certain stated intervals of repose — of recreation in the original sense of the word. My views on the worthlessness of classical education are perhaps pretty well known to you, but I don't underrate the great service that my friend Professor Ezra K. Higgins has rendered by his discovery[1] that the word recreation originally signified a re-creating — i.e.,[2] a time for the nerve-tissues to renew themselves in. The problem before us is how to secure for the human units in the Dawn — these giants of whom we are but the fœtuses — the holidays necessary for their full capacity for usefulness to the State, without at the same time disorganising the whole community — and them.

"The solution is really very simple. The community will be divided into ten sections

---

[1] "Words About Words." By Ezra K. Higgins, Professor of Etymology, Abraham Z. Stubbins University, Padua, Pa., U.S.A. (2 vols.).
[2] *"Id est"* — "That is."

— Section A, Section B, and so on to Section J. And to every section one day of the decimal week will be assigned as a 'Cessation Day.' Thus, those people who fall under Section A will rest on Aday, those who fall under Section B will rest on Bday, and so on. On every day of the year one-tenth of the population will be resting, but the other nine-tenths will be at work. The joyous hum and clang of labour will never cease in the municipal workshops. . . .

"You figure the smokeless blue sky above London dotted all over with airships in which the holiday-making tenth are re-creating themselves for the labour of next week — looking down a little wistfully, perhaps, at the workshops from which they are temporarily banished. And here I scent a difficulty. So attractive a thing will labour be in the Dawn that a man will be tempted not to knock off work when his Cessation Day comes round, and will prefer to work for no wage rather than not at all. So that perhaps there will have to be a law making Cessation Day compulsory, and the Overseers will be empowered to punish infringement of this law by forbidding the culprit to work for ten days after the first offence, twenty after the second, and so on. But I don't suppose there will often be need to put this law in motion. The children of the Dawn, remember, will not be the puny self-ridden creatures that we are. They will not say, 'Is this what I want to do?' but 'Shall I, by doing this, be (*a*) harming or (*b*) benefiting — no matter in how infinitesimal a degree — the Future of the Race?'

"Sunday must go. And, as I have hinted, the progress of mankind will be steady proportionately to its own automatism. Yet I think there would be no harm in having one — just one — day in the year set aside as a day of universal rest — a day for the searching of hearts. Heaven — I mean the Future — forbid that I should be hide-bound by dry-as-dust logic, in dealing with problems of flesh and blood. The sociologists of the past thought the grey matter of their own brains all-sufficing. They forgot that flesh is pink and blood is red. That is why they could not convert people. . . .

"The five-hundredth and last day of each year shall be a General Cessation Day. It will correspond somewhat to our present

[43]

Christmas Day. But with what a difference! It will not be, as with us, a mere opportunity for relatives to make up the quarrels they have picked with each other during the past year, and to eat and drink things that will make them ill well into next year. Holly and mistletoe there will be in the Municipal Eating Rooms, but the men and women who sit down there to General Cessation High-Tea will be glowing not with a facile affection for their kith and kin, but with communal anxiety for the welfare of the great-great-grand-children of people they have never met and are never likely to meet.

"The great event of the day will be the performance of the ceremony of 'Making Way.'

"In the Dawn, death will not be the haphazard affair that it is under the present anarchic conditions. Men will not be stumbling out of the world at odd moments and for reasons over which they have no control. There will always, of course, be a percentage of deaths by misadventure. But there will be no deaths by disease. Nor, on the other hand, will people die of old age. Every child will start life knowing that (barring mis-adventure) he has a certain fixed period of life before him — so much and no more, but not a moment less.

"It is impossible to foretell to what average age the children of the Dawn will retain the use of all their faculties — be fully vigorous mentally and physically. We only know they will be 'going strong' at ages when we have long ceased to be any use to the State. Let us, for sake of argument, say that on the average their faculties will have begun to decay at the age of ninety — a trifle over thirty-two, by the new reckoning. That, then, will be the period of life fixed for all citizens. Every man on fulfilling that period will avail himself of the Municipal Lethal Chamber. He will 'make way'. . . .

"I thought at one time that it would be best for every man to 'make way' on the actual day when he reaches the age-limit. But I see now that this would savour of private enterprise. Moreover, it would rule out that element of sentiment which, in relation to such a thing as death, we must do nothing to mar. The children and friends of a man on the brink of death would instinctively wish to gather round him. How could they accompany him to the lethal chamber, if it were an ordinary working-day, with every moment of the time mapped out for them ?

"On General Cessation Day, therefore, the gates of the lethal chambers will stand open for all those who shall in the course of the past year have reached the age-limit. You figure the wide streets filled all day long with little solemn processions — solemn and yet not in the least unhappy. . . . You figure the old man walking with a firm step in the midst of his progeny, looking around him with a clear eye at this dear world which is about to lose him. He will not be thinking of himself. He will not be wishing the way to the lethal chamber was longer. He will be filled with joy at the thought that he is about to die for the good of the race — to 'make way' for the beautiful young breed of men and women who, in simple, artistic, antiseptic garments, are disporting themselves so gladly on this day of days. They pause to salute him as he passes. And presently he sees, radiant in the sunlight, the pleasant white-tiled dome of the lethal chamber. You figure him at the gate, shaking hands all round, and speaking perhaps a few well-chosen words about the Future. . . ."

§5

It was enough. The old broom hadn't lost its snap. It had swept clean the chambers of Perkins' soul — swished away the whole accumulation of nasty little cobwebs and malignant germs. Gone were the mean doubts that had formed in him, the lethargy, the cheap cynicism. Perkins was himself again.

He saw now how very stupid it was of him to have despaired just because his own particular panacea wasn't given a chance. That Provisional Government plan of his had been good, but it was only one of an infinite number of possible paths to the Dawn. He would try others — scores of others . . . .

He must get right away out of here — to-night. He must have his car brought round from the garage — now — to a side door. . . .

But first he sat down to the writing-table, and wrote quickly :

Dear Duchess,

I regret I am called away on urgent political business. . . .

Yours faithfully

J. Perkins. . . .

He took the morocco leather case out of his pocket and enclosed it, with the note, in a large envelope.

Then he pressed the electric button by his bedside, almost feeling that this was a signal for the Dawn to rise without more ado. . . .

SOME DAMNABLE
ERRORS ABOUT
CHRISTMAS
By
G. K. CH*ST*RT*N

SOME DAMNABLE ERRORS
ABOUT CHRISTMAS

THAT it is human to err is admitted by
even the most positive of our thinkers.
Here we have the great difference between
latter-day thought and the thought of the
past. If Euclid were alive to-day (and I dare
say he is) he would not say, "The angles at
the base of an isosceles triangle are equal to
one another." He would say, "To me (a
very frail and fallible being, remember) it
does somehow seem that these two angles
have a mysterious and awful equality to one
another." The dislike of schoolboys for
Euclid is unreasonable in many ways; but
fundamentally it is entirely reasonable. Fundamentally it is the revolt from a man who
was either fallible and therefore (in pretend-
ing to infallibility) an impostor, or infallible
and therefore not human.

Now, since it is human to err, it is always
in reference to those things which arouse in
us the most human of all our emotions — I
mean the emotion of love — that we conceive

the deepest of our errors. Suppose we met Euclid on Westminster Bridge, and he took us aside and confessed to us that whilst he regarded parallelograms and rhomboids with an indifference bordering on contempt, for isosceles triangles he cherished a wild romantic devotion. Suppose he asked us to accompany him to the nearest music-shop, and there purchased a guitar in order that he might worthily sing to us the radiant beauty and the radiant goodness of isosceles triangles. As men we should, I hope, respect his enthusiasm, and encourage his enthusiasm, and catch his enthusiasm. But as seekers after truth we should be compelled to regard with a dark suspicion, and to check with the most anxious care, every fact that he told us about isosceles triangles. For adoration involves a glorious obliquity of vision. It involves more than that. We do not say of Love that he is short-sighted. We do not say of Love that he is myopic. We do not say of Love that he is astigmatic. We say quite simply, Love is blind. We might go further and say, Love is deaf. That would be a profound and obvious truth. We might go further still and say, Love is dumb. But hat would be a profound and obvious lie. For love is always an extraordinarily fluent talker. Love is a wind-bag, filled with a usty wind from Heaven.

It is always about the thing that we love most that we talk most. About this thing, therefore, our errors are something more than our deepest errors : they are our most frequent errors. That is why for nearly two thousand years mankind has been more glaringly wrong on the subject of Christmas than on any other subject. If mankind had hated Christmas, he would have understood it from the first. What would have happened then, it is impossible to say. For that which is hated, and therefore is persecuted, and therefore grows brave, lives on for ever, whilst that which is understood dies in the moment of our understanding of it — dies, as it were, in our awful grasp. Between the horns of this eternal dilemma shivers all the mystery of the jolly visible world, and of that still jollier world which is invisible. And it is because Mr. Shaw and the writers of his school cannot, with all their splendid sincerity and acumen, perceive that he and they and all of us are impaled on those horns as

certainly as the sausages I ate for breakfa
this morning had been impaled on the cook'
toasting-fork — it is for this reason, I say
that Mr. Shaw and his friends seem to m
to miss the basic principle that lies at th
root of all things human and divine. B
the way, not all things that are divine ar
human. But all things that are human ar
divine. But to return to Christmas.

I select at random two of the more obviou
fallacies that obtain. One is that Christma
should be observed as a time of jubilation
This is (I admit) quite a recent idea. I
never entered into the tousled heads of th
shepherds by night, when the light of th
angel of the Lord shone about them and the
arose and went to do homage to the Child
It never entered into the heads of the Thre
Wise Men. They did not bring their gift
as a joke, but as an awful oblation. It neve
entered into the heads of the saints and
scholars, the poets and painters, of the Middl
Ages. Looking back across the years, they
saw in that dark and ungarnished manger
only a shrinking woman, a brooding man
and a child born to sorrow. The philomaths
of the eighteenth century, looking back, saw

othing at all. It is not the least of the
lories of the Victorian Era that it redis-
overed Christmas. It is not the least of the
nistakes of the Victorian Era that it sup-
osed Christmas to be a feast.

The splendour of the saying, "I have piped
unto you, and you have not danced ; I have
vept with you, and you have not mourned"
ies in the fact that it might have been
uttered with equal truth by any man who
ad ever piped or wept. There is in the
human race some dark spirit of recalcitrance,
always pulling us in the direction contrary
to that in which we are reasonably expected
to go. At a funeral, the slightest thing, not
in the least ridiculous at any other time, will
convulse us with internal laughter. At a
wedding, we hover mysteriously on the brink
of tears. So it is with the modern Christmas.
I find myself in agreement with the cynics
in so far that I admit that Christmas, as now
observed, tends to create melancholy. But
the reason for this lies solely in our own
misconception. Christmas is essentially a
dies iræ. If the cynics will only make up
their minds to treat it as such, even the
saddest and most atrabilious of them will

acknowledge that he has had a rollicking
day.

This brings me to the second fallacy. I
refer to the belief that "Christmas comes but
once a year." Perhaps it does, according to
the calendar — a quaint and interesting compilation, but of little or no practical value to
anybody. It is not the calendar, but the
Spirit of Man that regulates the recurrence
of feasts and fasts. Spiritually, Christmas
Day recurs exactly seven times a week.
When we have frankly acknowledged this
and acted on this, we shall begin to realise
the Day's mystical and terrific beauty. For
it is only every-day things that reveal themselves to us in all their wonder and their
splendour. A man who happens one day
to be knocked down by a motor-bus merely
utters a curse and instructs his solicitor, but a
man who has been knocked down by a
motor-bus every day of the year will have
begun to feel that he is taking part in an
august and soul-cleansing ritual. He will
await the diurnal stroke of fate with the same
lowly and pious joy as animated the Hindoos
awaiting Juggernaut. His bruises will be
decorations, worn with the modest pride of

he veteran. He will cry aloud, in the words of the late W. E. Henley, "My head is bloody but unbowed." He will add, "My ribs are broken but unbent."

I look for the time when we shall wish one another a Merry Christmas every morning; when roast turkey and plum-pudding shall be the staple of our daily dinner, and the holly shall never be taken down from the walls, and everyone will always be kissing everyone else under the mistletoe. And what is right as regards Christmas is right as regards all other so-called anniversaries. The time will come when we shall dance round the Maypole every morning before breakfast — a meal at which hot-cross buns will be a standing dish — and shall make April fools of one another every day before noon. The profound significance of All Fool's Day — the glorious lesson that we are all fools — is too apt at present to be lost. Nor is justice done to the sublime symbolism of Shrove Tuesday — the day on which all sins are shriven. Every day pancakes shall be eaten, either before or after the plum-pudding. They shall be eaten slowly and sacramentally. They shall be fried over fires tended and kept

for ever bright by Vestals. They shall be
tossed to the stars.

I shall return to the subject of Christmas
next week.

A SEQUELULA TO
"THE DYNASTS"
By
TH*M*S H*RDY

A SEQUELULA TO "THE DYNASTS" [1]

The Void is disclosed. Our own Solar System is
    visible, distant by some two million miles.
Enter the Ancient Spirit and Chorus of the Years,
    the Spirit and Chorus of the Pities, the Spirit
    Ironic, the Spirit Sinister, Rumours, Spirit-Mes-
    sengers, and the Recording Angel.

SPIRIT OF THE PITIES.

Yonder, that swarm of things insectual
Wheeling Nowhither in Particular —
What is it?

SPIRIT OF THE YEARS.

*   That? Oh that is merely one*
Of those innumerous congeries
Of parasites by which, since time began,
Space has been interfested.

---

[1] *This has been composed from a scenario thrust*
on me by some one else. My philosophy of life saves
me from sense of responsibility for any of my writ-
ings ; but I venture to hold myself specially irrespon-
sible for this one.— TH✱M✱S H✱RDY.

[61]

SPIRIT SINISTER.

What a pity
We have no means of stamping out these
pests!

SPIRIT IRONIC.

Nay, but I like to watch them buzzing round,
Poor little trumpery ephaeonals!

CHORUS OF THE PITIES (aerial music).

Yes, yes!
What matter a few more or less?
Here and Nowhere plus
Whence and Why makes Thus.
Let these things be.
*There's room in the world for **them and us.***

Nothing is,
Out in the vast immensities
Where these things flit,
Irrequisite
In a minor key
*To the tune of the sempiternal **It.***

SPIRIT IRONIC.

The curious thing about them is that some
Have lesser parasites adherent to them —

Bipedular and quadrupedular
Infinitesimals. On close survey
You see these movesome. Do you not recall,
We once went in a party and beheld
All manner of absurd things happening
On one of those same — planets, don't you
* call them?*

SPIRIT OF THE YEARS (screwing up his eyes
          at the Solar System).

One of that very swarm it was, if I mistake
* not.*
It had a parasite that called itself
Napoléon. And lately, I believe,
Another parasite has had the impudence
To publish an elaborate account
Of our (for so we deemed it) private visit.

SPIRIT SINISTER.

His name?

RECORDING ANGEL.

One moment.

(Turns over leaves.)

          Hardy, Mr. Thomas,
Novelist. Author of "The Woodlanders,"
[63]

*"Far from the Madding Crowd," "The
    Trumpet Major,"
"Tess of the D'Urbervilles," etcetera,
Etcetera. In 1895
"Jude the Obscure" was published, and a
    few
Hasty reviewers, having to supply
A column for the day of publication,
Filled out their space by saying that there
    were
Several passages that might have been
Omitted with advantage. Mr. Hardy
Saw that if that was so, well then, of course,
Obviously the only thing to do
Was to write no more novels, and forthwith
Applied himself to drama, and to Us.*

SPIRIT IRONIC.

Let us hear what he said about Us.

THE OTHER SPIRITS.

                              Let's.

RECORDING ANGEL (raising receiver of aerial
                telephone).

*3 oh 4 oh oh 3 5, Space. . . . Hulloa.
Is that the Superstellar Library?*

'm the Recording Angel. Kindly send me
By Spirit-Messenger a copy of
'The Dynasts" by T. Hardy. Thank you.

A pause. Enter Spirit-Messenger, with copy
  of "The Dynasts."

Thanks.

Exit Spirit-Messenger. The Recording Angel reads
"The Dynasts" aloud.
Just as the reading draws to a close, enter the
  Spirit of Mr. Clement Shorter and Chorus of
  Subtershorters. They are visible as small grey
  transparencies swiftly interpenetrating the brains
  of the spatial Spirits.

SPIRIT OF THE PITIES.

It is a book which, once you take it up,
You cannot readily lay down.

SPIRIT SINISTER.

There is
Not a dull page in it.

SPIRIT OF THE YEARS.

A bold conception
Outcarried with that artistry for which
The author's name is guarantee. We have
No hesitation in commending to our readers
A volume which —

The spirit of Mr. Clement Shorter and Chorus of
    Subtershorters are detected and expelled.

             — we hasten to denounce
As giving an entirely false account
Of our impressions.

SPIRIT IRONIC.

Hear, *hear !*

SPIRIT SINISTER.

Hear, *hear !*

SPIRIT OF THE PITIES.

                          Hear !

SPIRIT OF THE YEARS.

Intensive vision has this Mr. Hardy,
With a dark skill in weaving word-patterns
Of subtle ideographies that mark him
A man of genius. So am not I,
But a plain Spirit, simple and forthright,
With no damned philosophical fal-lals
About me. When I visited that planet
And watched the animalculae thereon,
I never said they were "automata"
And "jackaclocks," nor dared describe their
    deeds

[66]

As "Life's impulsion by Incognizance."
It may be that those mites have no free will,
But how should I know? Nay, how Mr.
  Hardy?
We cannot glimpse the origin of things,
Cannot conceive a Causeless Cause, albeit
Such a Cause must have been, and must be
  greater
Than we whose little wits cannot conceive it.
"Incognizance"! Why deem incognizant
An infinitely higher than ourselves?
How dare define its way with us? How
  know
Whether it leaves us free or holds us bond?

SPIRIT OF THE PITIES.

Allow me to associate myself
With every word that's fallen from your lips.
The author of "The Dynasts" has indeed
Misused his undeniably great gifts
In striving to belittle things that are
Little enough already. I don't say
That the phrenetical behaviour
Of those aforesaid animalculae
Did, while we watched them, seem to
  indicate
Possession of free-will. But, bear in mind,

We saw them in peculiar circumstances —
At war, blinded with blood and lust and fear.
Is it not likely that at other times
They are quite decent midgets, capable
Of thinking for themselves, and also acting
Discreetly on their own initiative,
Not drilled and herded, yet gregarious —
A wise yet frolicsome community?

SPIRIT IRONIC.

What are these "other times" though? I
    had thought
Those midgets whiled away the vacuous
    hours
After one war in training for the next.
And let me add that my contempt for them
Is not done justice to by Mr. Hardy.

SPIRIT SINISTER.

Nor mine.   And I have reason to believe
Those midgets shone above their average
When we inspected them.

A RUMOUR (tactfully intervening).

                            Yet have I heard
(Though not on very good authority)
That once a year they hold a festival

And thereat all with one accord unite
In brotherly affection and good will.

SPIRIT OF THE YEARS (to Recording Angel).

Can you authenticate this Rumour?

RECORDING ANGEL.

Such festival they have, and call it "Christ-
mas."

SPIRIT OF THE PITIES.

Then let us go and reconsider them
Next "Christmas."

SPIRIT OF THE YEARS (to Recording Angel).

When is that?

RECORDING ANGEL (consults terrene calendar).

This day three weeks.

SPIRIT OF THE YEARS.

On that day we will re-traject ourselves.
Meanwhile, 'twere well we should be posted
up
In details of this feast.

[69]

SPIRIT OF THE PITIES (to Recording Angel)

Aye, tell us more.

RECORDING ANGEL.

I fancy you could best find what you need
In the Complete Works of the late Charles
    Dickens.
I have them here.

SPIRIT OF THE YEARS.

Read them aloud to us.

The Recording Angel reads aloud the Complete
    Works of Charles Dickens.

RECORDING ANGEL (closing "Edwin Drood")

'Tis Christmas Morning.

SPIRIT OF THE YEARS.

Then must we away.

SEMICHORUS I. OF YEARS (aerial music).

'Tis time we press on to revisit
  That dear little planet,
To-day of all days to be seen at
  Its brightest and best.

[70]

ow holly and mistletoe girdle
  Its halls and its homesteads,
nd every biped is beaming
  With peace and good will.

Semichorus II.

Vith good will and why not with free will?
  If clearly the former
May nest in those bosoms, then why not
  The latter as well?

Let's lay down no laws to trip up on,
  Our way is in darkness,
And not but by groping unhampered
  We win to the light.

The Spirit and Chorus of the Years traject themselves,
  closely followed by the Spirit and Chorus of the
  Pities, the Spirits and Choruses Sinister and
  Ironic, Rumours, Spirit Messengers, and the
  Recording Angel.

There is the sound of a rushing wind. The Solar
  System is seen for a few instants growing larger
  and larger — a whorl of dark, vastening orbs
  careering round the sun. All but one of these
  is lost to sight. The convex seas and continents
  of our planet spring into prominence.

The Spirit of Mr. Hardy is visible as a grey trans-
  parency swiftly interpenetrating the brain of the
  Spirit of the Years, and urging him in a particular direction, to a particular point.

The Aerial Visitants now hover in mid-air on the ou‍
skirts of Casterbridge, Wessex, immediate‍
above the County Gaol.

Spirit of the Years.

First let us watch the revelries within
This well-kept castle whose great walls con‍
    note
A home of the pre-eminently blest.

The roof of the gaol becomes transparent, and th‍
whole interior is revealed, like that of a be‍
hive under glass.
Warders are marching mechanically round the corr‍
dors of white stone, unlocking and clangin‍
open the iron doors of the cells. Out fro‍
every door steps a convict, who stands a‍
attention, his face to the wall.
At a word of command the convicts fall into gang‍
of twelve, and march down the stone stairs, ou‍
into the yard, where they line up against th‍
walls.
Another word of command, and they file mechan‍
cally, but not more mechanically than thei‍
warders, into the Chapel.

Spirit of the Pities.

Enough!

Spirits Sinister and Ironic.

'Tis more than even we can bear.

Spirit of the Pities.

Would we had never come!

Spirit of the Years.

Brother, 'tis well
To have faced a truth however hideous,
However humbling. Gladly I discipline
My pride by taking back those pettish doubts
Cast on the soundness of the central thought
In Mr. Hardy's drama. He was right.

Automata these animalculae
Are — puppets, pitiable jackaclocks.
Be't as it may elsewhere, upon this planet
There's no free will, only obedience
To some blind, deaf, unthinking despotry
That justifies the horridest pessimism.
Frankly acknowledging all this, I beat
A quick but not disorderly retreat.

He re-trajects himself into Space, followed closely by
his Chorus, and by the Spirit and Chorus of the
Pities, the Spirits Sinister and Ironic with their
Choruses, Rumours, Spirit Messengers, and the
Recording Angel.

SHAKESPEARE AND
CHRISTMAS
By
FR*NK H*RR*S

SHAKESPEARE AND CHRISTMAS

THAT Shakespeare hated Christmas — hated it with a venom utterly alien to the gentle heart in him — I take to be a proposition that establishes itself automatically. If there is one thing lucid-obvious in the Plays and Sonnets, it is Shakespeare's unconquerable loathing of Christmas. The Professors deny it, however, or deny that it is proven. With these gentlemen I will deal faithfully. I will meet them on their own parched ground, making them fertilise it by shedding there the last drop of the water that flows through their veins.

If you find, in the works of a poet whose instinct is to write about everything under the sun, one obvious theme untouched, or touched hardly at all, then it is at least presumable that there was some good reason for that abstinence. Such a poet was Shakespeare. It was one of the divine frailties of his genius that he must be ever flying off at a tangent from his main theme to unpack his heart in words about some frivolous-small irrelevance that had come into his head. If it could be shown that he never mentioned Christmas, we should have proof presumptive that he consciously avoided doing so. But if the fact is that he did mention it now and again, but in grudging fashion, without one spark of illumination — he, the arch-illuminator of all things — then we have proof positive that he detested it.

I see Dryasdust thumbing his Concordance. Let my memory save him the trouble. I will reel him off the one passage in which Shakespeare spoke of Christmas in words that rise to the level of mediocrity.

Some say that ever 'gainst that season comes
Wherein our Saviour's birth is celebrated,
The bird of dawning singeth all night long :
And then, they say, no spirit dare stir abroad ;
The nights are wholesome ; then no planets strike,
No fairy takes, nor witch hath power to charm,
So hallowed and so gracious is the time.

So says Marcellus at Elsinore. This is the best our Shakespeare can vamp up for the birthday of the Man with whom he of all men had the most in common. And Dryasdust, eternally unable to distinguish chalk from cheese, throws up his hands in admiration of the marvellous poetry. If Dryasdust had written it, it would more than pass muster. But as coming from Shakespeare, how feeble-cold — aye, and sulky-sinister! The greatest praiser the world will ever know! — and all he can find in his heart to sing of Christmas is a stringing-together of old women's superstitions! Again and again he has painted Winter for us as it never has been painted since — never by Goethe even, though Goethe in more than one of the *Winter-Lieder* touched the hem of his garment. There was every external reason why he should sing, as only he could have sung, of Christmas. The Queen set great store by it. She and her courtiers celebrated it year by year with lusty-pious unction. And thus the ineradicable snob in Shakespeare had the most potent of all inducements to honour the feast with the full power that was in him. But he did not, because he would not. What is the key to the enigma?

For many years I hunted it vainly. The second time that I met Carlyle I tried to enlist his sympathy and aid. He sat pensive for a while and then said that it seemed to him "a goose-quest." I replied, "You have always a phrase for everything, Tom, but always the wrong one." He covered his face, and presently, peering at me through his gnarled fingers, said "Mon, ye're recht." I discussed the problem with Renan, with Emerson, with Disraeli, also with Cetewayo — poor Cetewayo, best and bravest of men, but intellectually a Professor, like the rest of them. It was borne in on me that if I were to win to the heart of the mystery I must win alone.

The solution, when suddenly it dawned on me, was so simple-stark that I was ashamed of the ingenious-clever ways I had been following. (I learned then — and perhaps it is the one lesson worth the learning of any man — that truth may be approached only through the logic of the heart. For the heart is eye and ear, and all excellent understanding abides there.) On Christmas Day, assuredly, Anne Hathaway was born.

In what year she was born I do not know nor care. I take it she was not less than thirty-eight when she married Shakespeare. This, however, is sheer conjecture, and in no way important-apt to our inquiry. It is not the year, but the day of the year, that maters. All we need bear in mind is that on Christmas Day that woman was born into the world.

If there be any doubting Thomas among my readers, let him not be afraid to utter himself. I am (with the possible exception of Shakespeare) the gentlest man that ever breathed, and I do but bid him study the Plays in the light I have given him. The first thing that will strike him is that Shakespeare's thoughts turned constantly to the birthdays of all his Fitton-heroines, as a lover's thoughts always do turn to the moment at which the loved one first saw the light. "There was a star danced, and under that" was born Beatrice. Juliet was born "on Lammas Eve." Marina tells us she derived her name from the chance of her having been "born at sea." And so on, throughout the whole gamut of women in whom Mary Fitton was bodied forth to us. But mark how carefully Shakespeare says never a word about the birthdays of the various shrews and sluts in whom, again and again, he gave us his wife. When and where was born Queen Constance, the scold? And Bianca? And Doll Tearsheet, and "Greasy Jane" in the song, and all the rest of them ? It is of the last importance that we should know. Yet never a hint is vouchsafed us in the text. It is clear that Shakespeare cannot bring himself to write about Anne Hathaway's birthday — will not stain his imagination by thinking of it. That is entirely human natural. But why should he loathe Christmas Day itself with precisely the same loathing ? There is but one answer — and that inevitable-final. The two days were one.

Some soul-secrets are so terrible that the most hardened realist of us may well shrink from laying them bare. Such a soul-secret was this of Shakespeare's. Think of it ! The gentlest spirit that ever breathed, raging and fuming endlessly in impotent-bitter spleen against the prettiest of festivals ! Here is a spectacle so tragic-piteous that, try as we will, we shall not put it from us. And it is well that we should not, for in our plenary compassion we shall but learn to love the man the more.

[Mr. Fr*nk H*rr*s is very much a man of genius, and I should be sorry if this adumbration of his manner made any one suppose that I do not rate his writings about Shakespeare higher than those of all "the Professors" together.—M. B.]

SCRUTS
By
ARN*LD B*NN*TT

SCRUTS

I

EMILY WRACKGARTH stirred the Christmas pudding till her right arm began to ache. But she did not cease for that. She stirred on till her right arm grew so numb that it might have been the right arm of some girl at the other end of Bursley. And yet something deep down in her whispered "It is *your* right arm! And you can do what you like with it!"

She did what she liked with it. Relentlessly she kept it moving till it reasserted self as the arm of Emily Wrackgarth, prickling and tingling as with red-hot needles in every tendon from wrist to elbow. And still Emily Wrackgarth hardened her heart.

Presently she saw the spoon no longer revolving, but wavering aimlessly in the midst of the basin. Ridiculous! This must be seen to! In the down of dark hairs that connected her eyebrows there was a marked deepening of that vertical cleft which, visible at all times, warned you that here was a

[85]

young woman not to be trifled with. He[r]
brain despatched to her hand a peremptor[y]
message — which   miscarried. The   spoo[n]
wabbled as though held by a baby. Emil[y]
knew that she herself as a baby had been ca[r]
ried into this very kitchen to stir the Chris[t]
mas pudding. Year after year, as she gre[w]
up, she had been allowed to stir it "for luck[.]
And those, she reflected, were the only cook[-]
ery lessons she ever got. How like Mother[!]

Mrs. Wrackgarth had died in the past yea[r]
of a complication of ailments.[1] Emily sti[ll]
wore on her left shoulder that small tag [o]
crape which is as far as the Five Towns go [i]
the way of mourning. Her father had die[d]
in the year previous to that, of a still mor[e]
curious and enthralling complication of ai[l]
ments.[2] Jos, his son, carried on the Wrack[-]
garth Works, and Emily kept house for Jo[s]
She with her own hand had made this pud[-]
ding. But for her this pudding would n[ot]
have been. Fantastic ! Utterly incredible[!]
And yet so it was. She was grown-up. Sh[e]

[1] See "The History of Sarah Wrackgarth," p[.]
345-482.
[2] See "The History of Sarah Wrackgarth," p[.]
231-344.

as mistress of the house. She could make
or unmake puddings at will. And yet she
was Emily Wrackgarth. Which was absurd.

She would not try to explain, to reconcile.
She abandoned herself to the exquisite mysteries of existence. And yet in her abandonment she kept a sharp look-out on herself,
trying fiercely to make head or tail of her
nature. She thought herself a fool. But the
fact that she thought so was for her a proof
of adult sapience. Odd! She gave herself
up. And yet it was just by giving herself up
that she seemed to glimpse sometimes her
own inwardness. And these bleak revela-
tions saddened her. But she savoured her
sadness. It was the wine of life to her. And
for her sadness she scorned herself, and in her
conscious scorn she recovered her self-respect.
It is doubtful whether the people of
southern England have even yet realised how
much introspection there is going on all the
time in the Five Towns.

Visible from the window of the Wrack-
garths' parlour was that colossal statue of
Commerce which rears itself aloft at the
point where Oodge Lane is intersected by
Blackstead Street. Commerce, executed in

glossy Doultonware by some sculptor ∢
sculptors unknown, stands pointing h∈
thumb over her shoulder towards the chim
neys of far Hanbridge. When I tell you tha
the circumference of that thumb is si
inches, and the rest to scale, you will unde∫
stand that the statue is one of the prim∈
glories of Bursley. There were times whe∩
Emily Wrackgarth seemed to herself as va∫
and as lustrously impressive as it. Ther∈
were other times when she seemed to herse∣
as trivial and slavish as one of those perform
ing fleas she had seen at the Annual Ladie∫
Evening Fête organised by the Bursley M∪
tual Burial Club. Extremist !

She was now stirring the pudding with h∈
left hand. The ingredients had already be∈
mingled indistinguishably in that rich, u∩
dulating mass of tawniness which proclaim
perfection. But Emily was determined ⚹
give her left hand, not less than her righ
what she called "a doing." Emily was lik
that.

At mid-day, when her brother came hom∈
from the Works, she was still at it.

"Brought those scruts with you ?" sh∈
asked, without looking up.

"That's a fact," he said, dipping his hand into the sagging pocket of his coat.

It is perhaps necessary to explain what scruts are. In the daily output of every pot-bank there are a certain proportion of flawed vessels. These are cast aside by the foreman, with a lordly gesture, and in due course are hammered into fragments. These fragments, which are put to various uses, are called scruts; and one of the uses they are put to is a sentimental one. The dainty and luxurious Southerner looks to find in his Christmas pudding a wedding-ring, a gold thimble, a threepenny-bit, or the like. To such fal-lals the Five Towns would say fie. A Christmas pudding in the Five Towns contains nothing but suet, flour, lemon-peel, cinnamon, brandy, almonds, raisins — and two or three scruts. There is a world of poetry, beauty, romance, in scruts — though you have to have been brought up on them to appreciate it. Scruts have passed into the proverbial philosophy of the district. "Him's a pudden with more scruts than raisins to 'm" is a criticism not infrequently heard. It implies respect, even admiration. Of Emily Wrackgarth herself people often said, in reference to her likeness to her father, "Her's a scrut o' th' owd basin."

Jos had emptied out from his pocket on to the table a good three dozen of scruts. Emily laid aside her spoon, rubbed the palms of her hands on the bib of her apron, and proceeded to finger these scruts with the air of a connoisseur, rejecting one after another. The pudding was a small one, designed merely for herself and Jos, with remainder to "the girl"; so that it could hardly accommodate more than two or three scruts. Emily knew well that one scrut is as good as another. Yet she did not want her brother to feel that anything selected by him would necessarily pass muster with her. For his benefit she ostentatiously wrinkled her nose.

"By the by," said Jos, "you remember Albert Grapp? I've asked him to step over from Hanbridge and help eat our snack on Christmas Day."

Emily gave Jos one of her looks. "You've asked that Mr. Grapp?"

"No objection, I hope? He's not a bad sort. And he's considered a bit of a ladies' man, you know."

She gathered up all the scruts and let them all in a rattling shower on the exiguous pudding. Two or three fell wide of the basin. These she added.

"Steady on !" cried Jos. "What's that for ?"

"That's for your guest," replied his sister. 'And if you think you're going to palm me off on to him, or on to any other young fellow, you're a fool, Jos Wrackgarth."

The young man protested weakly, but she cut him short.

"Don't think," she said, "I don't know what you've been after, just of late. Cracking up one young sawny and then another on the chance of me marrying him ! I never heard of such goings on. But here I am, and here I'll stay, as sure as my name's Emily Wrackgarth, Jos Wrackgarth !"

She was the incarnation of the adorably feminine. She was exquisitely vital. She exuded at every pore the pathos of her young undirected force. It is difficult to write calmly about her. For her, in another age, ships would have been launched and cities besieged. But brothers are a race apart, and blind. It is a fact that Jos would have been glad to see his sister "settled"— preferably in one of the other four Towns.

She took up the spoon and stirred vigorously. The scruts grated and squeaked together around the basin, while the pudding feebly wormed its way up among them.

II

Albert Grapp, ladies' man though he was, was humble of heart. Nobody knew this but himself. Not one of his fellow clerks in Clither's Bank knew it. The general theory in Hanbridge was "Him's got a stiff opinion o' hisself." But this arose from what was really a sign of humility in him. He made the most of himself. He had, for instance, a way of his own in the matter of dressing. He always wore a voluminous frock-coat, with a pair of neatly-striped vicuna trousers, which he placed every night under his mattress, thus preserving in perfection the crease down the centre of each. His collar was of the highest, secured in front with an aluminium stud, to which was attached by a patent loop a natty bow of dove-coloured sateen. He had two caps, one of blue serge, the other of shepherd's plaid. These he wore on alternate days. He wore them in a way of his own — well back from his forehead, so as not to hide his hair, and with the peak behind. The peak made a sort of half-moon over the back of his collar. Through a fault of his tailor, there was a yawning gap between the back of his collar and the collar of his coat. Whenever he shook his head, the peak of his cap had the look of a live thing trying to investigate this abyss. Dimly aware of the effect, Albert Grapp shook his head as seldom as possible.

On wet days he wore a mackintosh. This, as he did not yet possess a great-coat, he wore also, but with less glory, on cold days. He had hoped there might be rain on Christmas morning. But there was no rain. "Like my luck," he said as he came out of his lodgings and turned his steps to that corner of Jubilee Avenue from which the Hanbridge-Bursley trams start every half-hour.

Since Jos Wrackgarth had introduced him to his sister at the Hanbridge Oddfellows' Biennial Hop, when he danced two quadrilles with her, he had seen her but once. He had nodded to her, Five Towns fashion, and she had nodded back at him, but with a look that

seemed to say "You needn't nod next time
you see me. I can get along well enough
without your nods." A frightening girl!
And yet her brother had since told him she
seemed "a bit gone, like" on him. Impossible! He, Albert Grapp, make an impression on the brilliant Miss Wrackgarth! Yet
she had sent him a verbal invite to spend
Christmas in her own home. And the time
had come. He was on his way. Incredible
that he should arrive! The tram must
surely overturn, or be struck by lightning.
And yet no! He arrived safely.

The small servant who opened the door
gave him another verbal message from Miss
Wrackgarth. It was that he must wipe his
feet "well" on the mat. In obeying this
order he experienced a thrill of satisfaction he
could not account for. He must have stood
shuffling his boots vigorously for a full minute. This, he told himself, was life. He,
Albert Grapp, was alive. And the world
was full of other men, all alive; and yet, because they were not doing Miss Wrackgarth's
bidding, none of them really lived. He was
filled with a vague melancholy. But his
melancholy pleased him.

In the parlour he found Jos awaiting him. The table was laid for three.

"So you're here, are you?" said the host, using the Five Towns formula. "Emily's in the kitchen," he added. "Happen she'll be here directly."

"I hope she's tol-lol-ish?" asked Albert.

"She is," said Jos. "But don't you go saying that to her. She doesn't care about society airs and graces. You'll make no headway if you aren't blunt."

"Oh, right you are," said Albert, with the air of a man who knew his way about.

A moment later Emily joined them, still wearing her kitchen apron. "So you're here, are you?" she said, but did not shake hands. The servant had followed her in with the tray, and the next few seconds were occupied in the disposal of the beef and trimmings.

The meal began, Emily carving. The main thought of a man less infatuated than Albert Grapp would have been "This girl can't cook. And she'll never learn to." The beef, instead of being red and brown, was pink and white. Uneatable beef! And yet he relished it more than anything he had ever tasted. This beef was her own handiwork. Thus it was because she had made it so. . . . He warily refrained from complimenting her, but the idea of a second helping obsessed him.

"Happen I could do with a bit more, like," he said.

Emily hacked off the bit more and jerked it on to the plate he had held out to her.

"Thanks," he said ; and then, as Emily's lip curled, and Jos gave him a warning kick under the table, he tried to look as if he had said nothing.

Only when the second course came on did he suspect that the meal was a calculated protest against his presence. This a Christmas pudding ? The litter of fractured earthenware was hardly held together by the suet and raisins. All his pride of manhood — and there was plenty of pride mixed up with Albert Grapp's humility — dictated a refusal to touch that pudding. Yet he soon found himself touching it, though gingerly, with his spoon and fork.

In the matter of dealing with scruts there are two schools — the old and the new. The old school pushes its head well over its plate and drops the scrut straight from its mouth. The new school emits the scrut into the fingers of its left hand and therewith deposits it on the rim of the plate. Albert noticed that Emily was of the new school. But might she not despise as affectation in him what came natural to herself? On the other hand, if he showed himself as a prop of the old school, might she not set her face the more stringently against him? The chances were that whichever course he took would be the wrong one.

It was then that he had an inspiration — an idea of the sort that comes to a man once in his life and finds him, likely as not, unable to put it into practice. Albert was not sure he could consummate this idea of his. He had indisputably fine teeth—"a proper mouthful of grinders" in local phrase. But would they stand the strain he was going to impose on them? He could but try them. Without a sign of nervousness he raised his spoon, with one scrut in it, to his mouth. This scrut he put between two of his left-side molars, bit hard on it, and — eternity of that moment! — felt it and heard it snap in two. Emily also heard it. He was conscious that at sound of the percussion she started forward

and stared at him. But he did not look at
her. Calmly, systematically, with gradually
diminishing crackles, he reduced that scrut
to powder, and washed the powder down
with a sip of beer. While he dealt with the
second scrut he talked to Jos about the Bor-
ough Council's proposal to erect an electric
power-station on the site of the old gas-
works down Hillport way. He was aware of
a slight abrasion inside his left cheek. No
matter. He must be more careful. There
were six scruts still to be negotiated. He
knew that what he was doing was a thing
grandiose, unique, epical ; a history-making
thing ; a thing that would outlive marble
and the gilded monuments of princes. Yet
he kept his head. He did not hurry, nor did
he dawdle. Scrut by scrut, he ground slowly
but he ground exceeding small. And while
he did so he talked wisely and well. He
passed from the power-station to a first edi-
tion of Leconte de Lisle's "Parnasse Contem-
porain" that he had picked up for sixpence
in Liverpool, and thence to the Midland's
proposal to drive a tunnel under the Knype
Canal so as to link up the main-line with the
Critchworth and Suddleford loop-line. Jos

was too amazed to put in a word. Jos sat merely gaping—a gape that merged by imperceptible degrees into a grin. Presently he ceased to watch his guest. He sat watching his sister.

Not once did Albert himself glance in her direction. She was just a dim silhouette on the outskirts of his vision. But there she was, unmoving, and he could feel the fixture of her unseen eyes. The time was at hand when he would have to meet those eyes. Would he flinch? Was he master of himself?

The last scrut was powder. No temporising! He jerked his glass to his mouth. A moment later, holding out his plate to her, he looked Emily full in the eyes. They were Emily's eyes, but not hers alone. They were collective eyes — that was it! They were the eyes of stark, staring womanhood. Her face had been dead white, but now suddenly up from her throat, over her cheeks, through the down between her eyebrows, went a rush of colour, up over her temples, through the very parting of her hair.

"Happen," he said without a quaver in his voice, "I'll have a bit more, like."

She flung her arms forward on the table and buried her face in them. It was a gesture wild and meek. It was the gesture foreseen and yet incredible. It was recondite, inexplicable, and yet obvious. It was the only thing to be done — and yet, by gum, she had done it.

Her brother had risen from his seat and was now at the door. "Think I'll step round to the Works," he said, "and see if they banked up that furnace aright."

NOTE.—*The author has in preparation a series of volumes dealing with the life of Albert and Emil Grapp.*

ENDEAVOUR
By
J*HN G*LSW*RTHY

ENDEAVOUR

THE dawn of Christmas Day found London laid out in a shroud of snow. Like body wasted by diseases that had triumphed over it at last, London lay stark and still now, beneath a sky that was as the closed leaden shell of a coffin. It was what is called an old-fashioned Christmas.

Nothing seemed to be moving except the Thames, whose embanked waters flowed on sullenly in their eternal act of escape to the sea. All along the wan stretch of Cheyne Walk the thin trees stood exanimate, with not a breath of wind to stir the snow that tied their soot-blackened branches. Here and there on the muffled ground lay a sparrow that had been frozen in the night, its little claws sticking up heavenward. But here and there also those tinier adventurers of the London air, smuts, floated vaguely and came to rest on the snow — signs that in the seeming death of civilisation some housemaids at least survived, and some fires had been lit.

One of these fires, crackling in the grat
of one of those dining-rooms which loo'
fondly out on the river and tolerantly acros
to Battersea, was being watched by the crit
ical eye of an aged canary. The cage i'
which this bird sat was hung in the middl
of the bow-window. It contained thre
perches, and also a pendent hoop. The tra
that was its floor had just been cleaned an'
sanded. In the embrasure to the right was
fresh supply of hemp-seed; in the embrasur
to the left the bath-tub had just been refille'
with clear water. Stuck between the bar
was a large sprig of groundsel. Yet, thoug'
all was thus in order, the bird did not eat no
drink, nor did he bathe. With his back t
Battersea, and his head sunk deep betwee'
his little sloping shoulders, he watched th
fire. The windows had for a while bee'
opened, as usual, to air the room for him
and the fire had not yet mitigated the chil'
It was not his custom to bathe at so inclemen
an hour; and his appetite for food and drink
less keen than it had once been, required t
be whetted by example — he never broke hi'
fast before his master and mistress brok
theirs. Time had been when, for sheer jo'

in life, he fluttered from perch to perch, though there were none to watch him, and even sang roulades, though there were none to hear. He would not do these things nowadays save at the fond instigation of Mr. and Mrs. Adrian Berridge. The housemaid who ministered to his cage, the parlourmaid who laid the Berridges' breakfast table, sometimes tried to incite him to perform for their own pleasure. But the sense of caste, strong in his protuberant little bosom, steeled him against these advances.

While the breakfast-table was being laid, he heard a faint tap against the window-pane. Turning round, he perceived on the sill a creature like to himself, but very different — a creature who, despite the pretensions of a red waistcoat in the worst possible taste, belonged evidently to the ranks of the outcast and the disinherited. In previous winters the sill had been strewn every morning with bread-crumbs. This winter, no bread-crumbs had been vouchsafed; and the canary, though he did not exactly understand why this was so, was glad that so it was. He had felt that his poor relations took advantage of the Berridges' kindness. Two or three of them, as pensioners, might not have been amiss. But they came in swarms, and they gobbled their food in a disgusting fashion, not trifling coquettishly with it as birds should. The reason for this, the canary knew, was that they were hungry; and of that he was sorry. He hated to think how much destitution there was in the world; and he could not help thinking about it when samples of it were thrust under his notice. That was the principal reason why he was glad that the window-sill was strewn no more and seldom visited.

He would much rather not have seen this solitary applicant. The two eyes fixed on his made him feel very uncomfortable. And yet, for fear of seeming to be outfaced, he did not like to look away.

The subdued clangour of the gong, sounded for breakfast, gave him an excuse for turning suddenly round and watching the door of the room.

A few moments later there came to him a faint odour of Harris tweed, followed immediately by the short, somewhat stout figure of his master—a man whose mild, fresh, pink, round face seemed to find salvation, as it were, at the last moment, in a neatly-pointed auburn beard.

Adrian Berridge paused on the threshold, as was his wont, with closed eyes and dilated nostrils, enjoying the aroma of complex fresh-ness which the dining-room had at this hour. Pathetically a creature of habit, he liked to savour the various scents, sweet or acrid, that went to symbolise for him the time and the place. Here were the immediate scents of dry toast, of China tea, of napery fresh from the wash, together with that vague, super-subtle scent which boiled eggs give out through their unbroken shells. And as a permanent base to these there was the scent of much-polished Chippendale, and of bees'-waxed parquet, and of Persian rugs. To-day, moreover, crowning the composition, there was the delicate pungency of the holly that topped the Queen Anne mirror and the Mantegna prints.

Coming forward into the room, Mr. Ber-ridge greeted the canary. "Well, Amber, old fellow," he said, "a happy Christmas to you!" Affectionately he pushed the tip of a plump white finger between the bars. "Tweet!" he added.

"Tweet!" answered the bird, hopping to and fro along his perch.

"Quite an old-fashioned Christmas, Amber!" said Mr. Berridge, turning to scan the weather. At sight of the robin, a little spasm of pain contracted his face. A shine of tears came to his prominent pale eyes, and he turned quickly away. Just at that moment, heralded by a slight fragrance of old lace and of that peculiar, almost unseizable odour that uncut turquoises have, Mrs. Berridge appeared.

"What is the matter, Adrian?" she asked quickly. She glanced sideways into the Queen Anne mirror, her hand fluttering, like a pale moth, to her hair, which she always wore braided in a fashion she had derived from Pollaiuolo's St. Ursula.

"Nothing, Jacynth — nothing," he answered with a lightness that carried no conviction; and he made behind his back a gesture to frighten away the robin.

"Amber isn't unwell, is he?" She came quickly to the cage. Amber executed for her a roulade of great sweetness. His voice had not perhaps the fullness for which it had been noted in earlier years; but the art with which he managed it was as exquisite as ever. It was clear to his audience that the veteran artist was hale and hearty.

But Jacynth, relieved on one point, had a misgiving on another. "This groundsel doesn't look very fresh, does it?" she murmured, withdrawing the sprig from the bars. She rang the bell, and when the servant came in answer to it said, "Oh Jenny, will you please bring up another piece of groundsel for Master Amber? I don't think this one is quite fresh."

This formal way of naming the canary to the servants always jarred on her principles and on those of her husband. They tried to regard their servants as essentially equals of themselves, and lately had given Jenny strict orders to leave off calling them "Sir" and "Ma'am," and to call them simply "Adrian" and "Jacynth." But Jenny, after one or two efforts that ended in faint giggles, had reverted to the crude old nomenclature — as much to the relief as to the mortification of the Berridges. They did, it is true, discuss the possibility of redressing the balance by calling the parlourmaid "Miss." But, when it came to the point, their lips refused this office. And conversely their lips persisted in the social prefix to the bird's name.

Somehow that anomaly seemed to them symbolic of their lives. Both of them yearned so wistfully to live always in accordance to the nature of things. And this, they felt, ought surely to be the line of least resistance. In the immense difficulties it presented, and in their constant failures to surmount these difficulties, they often wondered whether the nature of things might not be, after all, something other than what they thought it. Again and again it seemed to be in as direct conflict with duty as with inclination ; so that they were driven to wonder also whether what they conceived to be duty were not also a mirage — a marsh-light leading them on to disaster.

The fresh groundsel was brought in while Jacynth was pouring out the tea. She rose and took it to the cage ; and it was then that she too saw the robin, still fluttering on the sill. With a quick instinct she knew that Adrian had seen it — knew what had brought that look to his face. She went and, bending over him, laid a hand on his shoulder. The disturbance of her touch caused the tweed to give out a tremendous volume of scent, making her feel a little dizzy.

"Adrian," she faltered, "mightn't we for once — it is Christmas Day — mightn't we, just to-day, sprinkle some bread-crumbs?"

He rose from the table, and leaned against the mantelpiece, looking down at the fire. She watched him tensely. At length, "Oh Jacynth," he groaned, "don't — don't tempt me."

"But surely, dear, surely ——"

"Jacynth, don't you remember that long talk we had last winter, after the annual meeting of the Feathered Friends' League, and how we agreed that those sporadic doles could do no real good — must even degrade the birds who received them — and that we had no right to meddle in what ought to be done by collective action of the State?"

"Yes, and — oh my dear, I do still agree, with all my heart. But if the State will do nothing — nothing ——"

"It won't, it daren't, go on doing nothing, unless we encourage it to do so. Don't you see, Jacynth, it is just because so many people take it on themselves to feed a few birds here and there that the State feels it can afford to shirk the responsibility ?"

"All that is fearfully true. But just now — Adrian, the look in that robin's eyes ——"

Berridge covered his own eyes, as though to blot out from his mind the memory of that look. But Jacynth was not silenced. She felt herself dragged on by her sense of duty to savour, and to make her husband savour, the full bitterness that the situation could yield for them both. "Adrian," she said, "a fearful thought came to me. Suppose — suppose it had been Amber !"

Even before he shuddered at the thought, he raised his finger to his lips, glancing round at the cage. It was clear that Amber had not overheard Jacynth's remark, for he threw back his head and uttered one of his blithest trills. Adrian, thus relieved, was free to shudder at the thought just suggested.

"Sometimes," murmured Jacynth, "I wonder if we, holding the views we hold, are justified in keeping Amber."

"Ah, dear, we took him in our individualistic days. We cannot repudiate him now. It wouldn't be fair. Besides, you see, he isn't here on a basis of mere charity. He's not a parasite, but an artist. He gives us of his art."

"Yes, dear, I know. But you remember our doubts about the position of artists in the community — whether the State ought to sanction them at all."

"True. But we cannot visit those doubts on our old friend yonder, can we, dear? At the same time, I admit that when — when — Jacynth, if ever anything happens to Amber, we shall perhaps not be justified in keeping another bird."

"Don't, please don't talk of such things." She moved to the window. Snow, a delicate white powder, was falling on the coverlet of snow.

Outside, on the sill, the importunate robin lay supine, his little heart beating no more behind the shabby finery of his breast, but his glazing eyes half-open as though even in death he were still questioning. Above him and all around him brooded the genius of infinity, dispassionate, inscrutable, grey.

Jacynth turned and mutely beckoned her husband to the window.

They stood there, these two, gazing silently down.

[113]

Presently Jacynth said : "Adrian, are you sure that we, you and I, for all our theories and all our efforts, aren't futile ?"

"No, dear. Sometimes I am not sure. But — there's a certain comfort in not being sure. To die for what one knows to be true — as many saints have done — that is well. But to live, as many of us do nowadays, in service of what may, for aught we know, be only a half-truth or not true at all — this seems to me nobler still."

"Because it takes more out of us ?"

"Because it takes more out of us."

Standing between the live bird and the dead, they gazed across the river, over the snow-covered wharves, over the dim, slender chimneys from which no smoke came, into the grey-black veil of the distance. And it seemed to them that the genius of infinity did not know — perhaps did not even care — whether they were futile or not, nor how much and to what purpose, if to any purpose, they must go on striving.

CHRISTMAS

By

G. S. STR**T

CHRISTMAS

ONE likes it or not. This said, there is plaguey little else to say of Christmas, and I (though I doubt my sentiments touch you not at all) would rather leave that little unsaid. Did I confess a distaste for Christmas, I should incur your enmity. But if I had it, as I protest I do, rather agreeable than otherwise, why should I spoil my pleasure by ringing vain words about it? Swift and the broomstick — yes. But that essay was done at the behest of a clever woman, and to annoy the admirers of Robert Boyle. Besides, it was hardly — or do you think it was? — worth the trouble of doing it. There was no trouble involved? Possibly. But I am not the Dean. And anyhow the fact that he never did anything of the kind again may be taken to imply that he would not be bothered. So would not I, if I had a deanery.

That is an hypothesis I am tempted to pursue. I should like to fill my allotted space before reaching the tiresome theme I

have set myself . . . A deanery, the cawing
of rooks, their effect on the nervous system,
Trollope's delineations of deans, the advan-
tages of the Mid-Victorian novel . . . But
your discursive essayist is a nuisance. Better
come to the point. The bore is in finding a
point to come to. Besides, the chances are
that any such point will have long ago been
worn blunt by a score of more active seekers.
Alas !

Since I wrote the foregoing words, I have
been out for a long walk, in search of inspiration, through the streets of what is called the
West End. Snobbishly so called. Why
draw these crude distinctions ? We all know
that Mayfair happens to lie a few miles further west than Whitechapel. It argues a lack
of breeding to go on calling attention to the
fact. If the people of Whitechapel were less
beautiful or less well-mannered or more igno-
rant than we, there might be some excuse.
But they are not so. True, themselves talk
about the East End, but this only makes the
matter worse. To a sensitive ear their phrase
has a ring of ironic humility that jars no
less than our own coarse boastfulness.
Heaven knows they have a right to be ironic.

d who shall blame them for exercising it?
l the same, this sort of thing worries me
rribly.

I said that I found Christmas rather agree-
le than otherwise. But I was speaking as
e accustomed to live mostly in the past.
he walk I have just taken, refreshing in
elf, has painfully reminded me that I can-
t hit it off with the present. My life is in
e later days of the eighteenth and the
rlier days of the nineteenth century. This
ventieth affair is as a vision, dimly foreseen
odd moments, and put from me with a
ight shudder. My actual Christmases are
ent (say) in Holland House, which has
ut recently been built. Little Charles Fox
allowed by his father to join us for the
rlier stages of dessert. I am conscious of
atting him on the head and predicting for
im a distinguished future. A very bright
ttle fellow, with his father's eyes! Or
gain, I am down at Newstead. Byron is
his wildest spirits, a shade too uproarious.
am glad to escape into the park and stroll
quiet hour on the arm of Mr. Hughes Ball.
ears pass. The approach of Christmas
nds one loth to leave one's usual haunts.

One is on one's way to one's club to di[n]
with Postumus and dear old "Wigsby" Pe[n]
dennis, quietly at one's consecrated table ne[ar]
the fireplace. As one is crossing St. James[']
Street an ear-piercing grunt causes one to re[el]
back just in time to be not run over by [a]
motor-car. Inside is a woman who scow[ls]
down at one through the window — "Ser[ve]
you right if we'd gone over you." Yes, [one]
often have these awakenings to fact — [or]
rather these provisions of what life mig[ht]
be if I survived into the twentieth centur[y]
Alas !

I have mentioned that woman in t[he]
motor-car because she is germane to m[y]
theme. She typifies the vices of the moder[n]
Christmas. For her, by the absurd accide[nt]
of her wealth, there is no distinction betwee[n]
people who have not motor-cars and peop[le]
who might as well be run over. But I wron[g]
her. If we others were all run over, the[re]
would be no one before whom she coul[d]
flaunt her loathsome air of superiority. An[d]
what would she do then, poor thing ? [I]
doubt she would die of boredom — painfull[y]
one hopes. In the same way, if the sho[p]
keepers in Bond Street knew there was n[o]

one who could not afford to buy the things
in their windows, there would be an end to
the display that makes those windows intoler-
able (to you and me) during the month of
December. I had often suspected that the
things there were not meant to be bought by
people who could buy them, but merely to
irritate the rest. This afternoon I was sure
of it. Not in one window anything a sane
person would give to any one not an idiot,
but everywhere a general glossy grin out at
people who are not plutocrats. This sort of
thing lashes me to ungovernable fury. The
lion is roused, and I recognise in myself a
born leader of men. Be so good as to smash
those windows for me.

One does not like to think that Christmas
has been snapped up, docked of its old-world
kindliness, and pressed into the service of an
odious ostentation. But so it has. Alas!
The thought of Father Christmas trudging
through the snow to the homes of gentle
and simple alike (forgive that stupid, snob-
bish phrase) was agreeable. But Father
Christmas in red plush breeches, lounging on
the doorstep of Sir Gorgius Midas — one
averts one's eyes.

I have — now I come to think of it — another objection to the modern Christmas. It would be affectation to pretend not to know that there are many Jews living in England, and in London especially. I have always had a deep respect for that race, their distinction in intellect and in character. Being not one of them, I may in their behalf put a point which themselves would be the last to suggest. I hope they will acquit me of impertinence in doing this. You, in your turn, must acquit me of sentimentalism. The Jews are a minority, and as such must take their chances. But may not a majority refrain from pressing its rights to the utmost? It is well that we should celebrate Christmas heartily, and all that. But we could do so without an emphasis that seems to me, in the circumstances, 'tother side good taste. "Good taste" is a hateful phrase. But it escaped me in the heat of the moment. Alas !

THE FEAST
By
J*S*PH C*NR*D

THE FEAST

THE hut in which slept the white man was on a clearing between the forest and the river. Silence, the silence murmurous and unquiet of a tropical night, brooded over the hut that, baked through by the sun, sweated a vapour beneath the cynical light of the stars. Mahamo lay rigid and watchful at the hut's mouth. In his upturned eyes, and along the polished surface of his lean body black and immobile, the stars were reflected, creating an illusion of themselves who are illusions.

The roofs of the congested trees, writhing in some kind of agony private and eternal, made tenebrous and shifty silhouettes against the sky, like shapes cut out of black paper by a maniac who pushes them with his thumb this way and that, irritably, on a concave surface of blue steel. Resin oozed unseen from the upper branches to the trunks swathed in creepers that clutched and interlocked with tendrils venomous, frantic and faint. Down below, by force of habit, the lush herbage went through the farce of

[125]

growth — that farce old and screaming, whose trite end is decomposition.

Within the hut the form of the white man, corpulent and pale, was covered with a mosquito-net that was itself illusory like everything else, only more so. Flying squadrons of mosquitoes inside its meshes flickered and darted over him, working hard, but keeping silence so as not to excite him from sleep. Cohorts of yellow ants disputed him against cohorts of purple ants, the two kinds slaying one another in thousands. The battle was undecided when suddenly, with no such warning as it gives in some parts of the world, the sun blazed up over the horizon, turning night into day, and the insects vanished back into their camps.

The white man ground his knuckles into the corners of his eyes, emitting that snore final and querulous of a middle-aged man awakened rudely. With a gesture brusque but flaccid he plucked aside the net and peered around. The bales of cotton cloth, the beads, the brass wire, the bottles of rum, had not been spirited away in the night. So far so good. The faithful servant of his employers was now at liberty to care for his own interests. He regarded himself, passing his hands over his skin.

"Hi! Mahamo!" he shouted. "I've been eaten up."

The islander, with one sinuous motion, sprang from the ground, through the mouth of the hut. Then, after a glance, he threw high his hands in thanks to such good and evil spirits as had charge of his concerns. In a tone half of reproach, half of apology, he murmured —

"You white men sometimes say strange things that deceive the heart."

"Reach me that ammonia bottle, d'you hear?" answered the white man. "This is a pretty place you've brought me to!" He took a draught. "Christmas Day, too! Of all the —— But I suppose it seems all right to you, you funny blackamoor, to be here on Christmas Day?"

"We are here on the day appointed, Mr. Williams. It is a feast-day of your people?"

Mr. Williams had lain back, with closed eyes, on his mat. Nostalgia was doing duty to him for imagination. He was wafted to a bedroom in Marylebone, where in honour of the Day he lay late dozing, with great contentment; outside, a slush of snow in the street, the sound of churchbells; from below a savour of especial cookery. "Yes," he said, "it's a feast-day of my people."

"Of mine also," said the islander humbly.

"Is it though? But they'll do business first?"

"They must first do that."

"And they'll bring their ivory with them?"

"Every man will bring ivory," answered the islander, with a smile gleaming and wide.

"How soon'll they be here?"

"Has not the sun risen? They are on their way."

"Well, I hope they'll hurry. The sooner we're off this cursed island of yours the better. Take all those things out," Mr. Williams added, pointing to the merchandise, "and arrange them — neatly, mind you!"

In certain circumstances it is right that a man be humoured in trifles. Mahamo, having borne out the merchandise, arranged it very neatly.

While Mr. Williams made his toilet, the sun and the forest, careless of the doings of white and black men alike, waged their warfare implacable and daily. The forest from its inmost depths sent forth perpetually its legions of shadows that fell dead in the instant of exposure to the enemy whose rays heroic and absurd its outposts annihilated. There came from those inilluminable depths the equable rumour of myriads of winged things and crawling things newly roused to the task of killing and being killed. Thence detached itself, little by little, an insidious sound of a drum beaten. This sound drew more near.

Mr. Williams, issuing from the hut, heard it, and stood gaping towards it.

"Is that them ?" he asked.

"That is they," the islander murmured, moving away towards the edge of the forest.

Sounds of chanting were a now audible accompaniment to the drum.

"What's that they're singing ?" asked Mr. Williams.

"They sing of their business," said Mahamo.

"Oh !" Mr. Williams was slightly shocked. "I'd have thought they'd be singing of their feast."

"It is of their feast they sing."

It has been stated that Mr. Williams was

not imaginative. But a few years of life in climates alien and intemperate had disordered his nerves. There was that in the rhythms of the hymn which made bristle his flesh.

Suddenly, when they were very near, the voices ceased, leaving a legacy of silence more sinister than themselves. And now the black spaces between the trees were relieved by bits of white that were the eyeballs and teeth of Mahamo's brethren.

"It was of their feast, it was of you, they sang," said Mahamo.

"Look here," cried Mr. Williams in his voice of a man not to be trifled with. "Look here, if you've ——"

He was silenced by sight of what seemed to be a young sapling sprung up from the ground within a yard of him — a young sapling tremulous, with a root of steel. Then a thread-like shadow skimmed the air, and another spear came impinging the ground within an inch of his feet.

As he turned in his flight he saw the goods so neatly arranged at his orders, and there flashed through him, even in the thick of the spears, the thought that he would be a

[130]

grave loss to his employers. This — for Mr. Williams was, not less than the goods, of a kind easily replaced — was an illusion. It was the last of Mr. Williams' illusions.

A RECOLLECTION
By
EDM*ND G*SSE

A RECOLLECTION

"And let us strew
Twain wreaths of holly and of yew."
WALLER.

ONE out of many Christmas Days abides
with peculiar vividness in my memory.
In setting down, however clumsily, some
slight record of it, I feel that I shall be dis-
charging a duty not only to the two dis-
parately illustrious men who made it so very
memorable, but also to all young students of
English and Scandinavian literature. My use
of the first person singular, delightful though
that pronoun is in the works of the truly
gifted, jars unspeakably on me; but reasons
of space baulk my sober desire to call myself
merely the present writer, or the infatuated
go-between, or the cowed and imponderable
young person who was in attendance.

In the third week of December, 1878, taking the opportunity of a brief and undeserved
vacation, I went to Venice. On the morning
after my arrival, in answer to a most kind
and cordial summons, I presented myself at

the Palazzo Rezzonico. Intense as was the
impression he always made even in London,
I think that those of us who met Robert
Browning only in the stress and roar of that
metropolis can hardly have gauged the fullness of his potentialities for impressing.
Venice, "so weak, so quiet," as Mr. Ruskin
had called her, was indeed the ideal setting
for one to whom neither of those epithets
could by any possibility have been deemed
applicable. The steamboats that now wake
the echoes of the canals had not yet been
imported; but the vitality of the imported
poet was in some measure a preparation for
them. It did not, however, find me quite
prepared for itself, and I am afraid that
some minutes must have elapsed before I
could, as it were, find my feet in the torrent
of his geniality and high spirits, and give
him news of his friends in London.

He was at that time engaged in revising
the proof-sheets of "Dramatic Idylls," and
after luncheon, to which he very kindly bade
me remain, he read aloud certain selected
passages. The yellow haze of a wintry Venetian sunshine poured in through the vast
windows of his *salone,* making an aureole

around his silvered head. I would give much to live that hour over again. But it was vouchsafed in days before the Browning Society came and made everything so simple for us all. I am afraid that after a few minutes I sat enraptured by the sound rather than by the sense of the lines. I find, in the notes I made of the occasion, that I figured myself as plunging through some enchanted thicket on the back of an inspired bull.

That evening, as I was strolling in Piazza San Marco, my thoughts of Browning were all of a sudden scattered by the vision of a small, thick-set man seated at one of the tables in the Café Florian. This was — and my heart leapt like a young trout when I saw that it could be none other than — Henrik Ibsen. Whether joy or fear was the predominant emotion in me, I should be hard put to it to say. It had been my privilege to correspond extensively with the great Scandinavian, and to be frequently received by him, some years earlier than the date of which I write, in Rome. In that city haunted by the shades of so many Emperors and Popes I had felt comparatively at ease even in Ibsen's presence. But seated here in

the homelier decay of Venice, closely but-
toned in his black surcoat and crowned with
his uncompromising top-hat, with the lights
of the Piazza flashing back wanly from his
gold-rimmed spectacles, and his lips tight-
shut like some steel trap into which our poor
humanity had just fallen, he seemed to con-
stitute a menace under which the boldest
might well quail. Nevertheless, I took my
courage in both hands, and laid it as a kind
of votive offering on the little table before
him.

My reward was in the surprising amiability
that he then and afterwards displayed. My
travelling had indeed been doubly blessed,
for, whilst my subsequent afternoons were
spent in Browning's presence, my evenings
fell with regularity into the charge of Ibsen.
One of these evenings is for me "prouder,
more laurel'd than the rest" as having been
the occasion when he read to me the MS. of
a play which he had just completed. He
was staying at the Hôtel Danieli, an edifice
famous for having been, rather more than
forty years previously, the socket in which
the flame of an historic *grande passion* had
finally sunk and guttered out with no incon-

siderable accompaniment of smoke and odour. It was there, in an upper room, that I now made acquaintance with a couple very different from George Sand and Alfred de Musset, though destined to become hardly less famous than they. I refer to Torvald and Nora Helmer. My host read to me with the utmost vivacity, standing in the middle of the apartment; and I remember that in the scene where Nora Helmer dances the tarantella her creator instinctively executed a few illustrative steps.

During those days I felt very much as might a minnow swimming to and fro between Leviathan on the one hand and Behemoth on the other — a minnow tremulously pleased, but ever wistful for some means of bringing his two enormous acquaintances together. On the afternoon of December 24th I confided to Browning my aspiration. He had never heard of this brother poet and dramatist, whose fame indeed was at that time still mainly Boreal; but he cried out with the greatest heartiness, "Capital! Bring him round with you at one o'clock to-morrow for turkey and plum-pudding!"

I betook myself straight to the Hôtel
Danieli, hoping against hope that Ibsen's sole
answer would not be a comminatory grunt
and an instant rupture of all future relations
with myself. At first he was indeed resolute
not to go. He had never heard of this Herr
Browning. (It was one of the strengths of
his strange, crustacean genius that he never
had heard of anybody.) I took it on myself
to say that Herr Browning would send his
private gondola, propelled by his two gon-
doliers, to conduct Herr Ibsen to the scene
of the festivity. I think it was this prospect
that made him gradually unbend, for he had
already acquired that taste for pomp and cir-
cumstance which was so notable a characteristic of his later years. I hastened back to
the Palazzo Rezzonico before he could change
his mind. I need hardly say that Browning
instantly consented to send the gondola. So
large and lovable was his nature that, had he
owned a thousand of those conveyances, he
would not have hesitated to send out the
whole fleet in honour of any friend of any
friend of his.

Next day, as I followed Ibsen down the
Danielian water-steps into the expectant gon-

dola, my emotion was such that I was tempted to snatch from him his neatly-furled umbrella and spread it out over his head, like the umbrella beneath which the Doges of days gone by had made their appearances in public. It was perhaps a pity that I repressed this impulse. Ibsen seemed to be already regretting that he had unbent. I could not help thinking, as we floated along the Riva Schiavoni, that he looked like some particularly ruthless member of the Council of Ten. I did, however, try faintly to attune him in some sort to the spirit of our host and of the day of the year. I adumbrated Browning's outlook on life, translating into Norwegian, I well remember, the words "God's in His heaven, all's right with the world." In fact I cannot charge myself with not having done what I could. I can only lament that it was not enough.

When we marched into the *salone,* Browning was seated at the piano, playing (I think) a Toccata of Galuppi's. On seeing us, he brought his hands down with a great crash on the keyboard, seemed to reach us in one astonishing bound across the marble floor, and clapped Ibsen loudly on either shoulder,

[141]

wishing him "the Merriest of Merry Christmases."

Ibsen, under this sudden impact, stood firm as a rock, and it flitted through my brain that here at last was solved the old problem of what would happen if an irresistible force met an immoveable mass. But it was obvious that the rock was not rejoicing in the moment of victory. I was tartly asked whether I had not explained to Herr Browning that his guest did not understand English. I hastily rectified my omission, and thenceforth our host spoke in Italian. Ibsen, though he understood that language fairly well, was averse to speaking it. Such remarks as he made in the course of the meal to which we presently sat down were made in Norwegian and translated by myself.

Browning, while he was carving the turkey, asked Ibsen whether he had visited any of the Venetian theatres. Ibsen's reply was that he never visited theatres. Browning laughed his great laugh, and cried "That's right! We poets who write plays must give the theatres as wide a berth as possible. We aren't wanted there!" "How so?" asked Ibsen. Browning looked a little puzzled, and I had to explain that in northern Europe Herr Ibsen's plays were frequently performed. At this I seemed to see on Browning's face a slight shadow — so swift and transient a shadow as might be cast by a swallow flying across a sunlit garden. An instant, and it was gone. I was glad, however, to be able to soften my statement by adding that Herr Ibsen had in his recent plays abandoned the use of verse.

The trouble was that in Browning's company he seemed practically to have abandoned the use of prose too. When, moreover, he did speak, it was always in a sense contrary to that of our host. The Risorgimento was a theme always very near to the great heart of Browning, and on this occasion he hymned it with more than his usual animation and resource (if indeed that were possible). He descanted especially on the vast increase that had accrued to the sum of human happiness in Italy since the success of that remarkable movement. When Ibsen rapped out the conviction that what Italy needed was to be invaded and conquered once and for all by Austria, I feared that an explosion was inevitable. But hardly had

[143]

my translation of the inauspicious sentiment
been uttered when the plum-pudding was
borne into the room, flaming on its dish. I
clapped my hands wildly at sight of it, in the
English fashion, and was intensely relieved
when the yet more resonant applause of
Robert Browning followed mine. Disaster
had been averted by a crowning mercy. But
I am afraid that Ibsen thought us both quite
mad.

The next topic that was started, harmless
though it seemed at first, was fraught with
yet graver peril. The world of scholarship
was at that time agitated by the recent discovery of what might or might not prove
to be a fragment of Sappho. Browning proclaimed his unshakeable belief in the au-
thenticity of these verses. To my surprise,
Ibsen, whom I had been unprepared to regard as a classical scholar, said positively that
they had not been written by Sappho.
Browning challenged him to give a reason.
A literal translation of the reply would have
been "Because no woman ever was capable of
writing a fragment of good poetry." Imagination reels at the effect this would
have had on the recipient of "Sonnets from

the Portuguese." The agonised interpreter, throwing honour to the winds, babbled some wholly fallacious version of the words. Again the situation had been saved; but it was of the kind that does not even in furthest retrospect lose its power to freeze the heart and constrict the diaphragm.

I was fain to thank heaven when, immediately after the termination of the meal, Ibsen rose, bowed to his host, and bade me express his thanks for the entertainment. Out on the Grand Canal, in the gondola which had again been placed at our disposal, his passion for "documents" that might bear on his work was quickly manifested. He asked me whether Herr Browning had ever married. Receiving an emphatically affirmative reply, he inquired whether Fru Browning had been happy. Loth though I was to cast a blight on his interest in the matter, I conveyed to him with all possible directness the impression that Elizabeth Barrett had assuredly been one of those wives who do not dance tarantellas nor slam front-doors. He did not, to the best of my recollection, make further mention of Browning, either then or afterwards. Browning himself, however, thanked me warmly, next day, for having introduced my friend to him. "A capital fellow!" he exclaimed, and then, for a moment, seemed as though he were about to qualify this estimate, but ended by merely repeating "A capital fellow!"

Ibsen remained in Venice some weeks after my return to London. He was, it may be conjectured, bent on a specially close study of the Bride of the Adriatic because her marriage had been not altogether a happy one. But there appears to be no evidence whatsoever that he went again, either of his own accord or by invitation, to the Palazzo Rezzonico.

OF CHRISTMAS
By
H*L**RE B*LL*C

OF CHRISTMAS

THERE was a man came to an Inn by
night, and after he had called three
times they should open him the door —
though why three times, and not three times
three, nor thirty times thirty, which is the
number of the little stone devils that make
mows at St. Aloesius of Ledera over against
the marshes Gué-la-Nuce to this day, nor
three hundred times three hundred (which is
a bestial number), nor three thousand times
three-and-thirty, upon my soul I know not,
and nor do you — when, then, this jolly fellow had three times cried out, shouted, yelled,
holloa'd, loudly besought, caterwauled,
brayed, sung out, and roared, he did by the
same token set himself to beat, hammer,
bang, pummel, and knock at the door.
Now the door was Oak. It had been grown
in the forest of Boulevoise, hewn in Barre-le-
Neuf, seasoned in South Hoxton, hinged
nowhere in particular, and panelled — and
that most abominably well — in Arque,
where the peasants sell their souls for skill in

such handicraft. But our man knew nothing
of all this, which, had he known it, would
have mattered little enough to him, for a
reason which I propose to tell in the next
sentence. The door was opened. As to the
reasons why it was not opened sooner, these
are most tediously set forth in Professor Sir
T. K. Slibby's "Half-Hours With Historic
Doors," as also in a fragment at one time
attributed to Oleaginus Silo but now proven
a forgery by Miss Evans. Enough for our
purpose, merry reader of mine, that the door
was opened.

The man, as men will, went in. And
there, for God's sake and by the grace of
Mary Mother, let us leave him; for the truth
of it is that his strength was all in his lungs
and himself a poor, weak, clout-faced, wizen-
bellied, pin-shanked bloke anyway, who at
Trinity Hall had spent the most of his time
in reading Hume (that was Satan's lackey),
and after taking his degree did a little in the
way of Imperial Finance. Of him it was
that Lord Abraham Hart, that far-seeing
statesman, said, "This young man has the
root of the matter in him." I quote the epi-
gram rather for its perfect form than for its

truth. For once, Lord Abraham was deceived. But it must be remembered that he was at this time being plagued almost out of his wits by the vile (though cleverly engineered) agitation for the compulsory winding-up of the Rondoosdop Development Company. Afterwards, in Wormwood Scrubbs, his Lordship admitted that his estimate of his young friend had perhaps been pitched too high. In Dartmoor he has since revoked it altogether, with that manliness for which the Empire so loved him when he was at large.

Now the young man's name was Dimby —"Trot" Dimby — and his mother had been a Clupton, so that — but had I not already dismissed him? Indeed I only mentioned him because it seemed that his going to that Inn might put me on track of that One Great Ultimate and Final True Thing I am purposed to say about Christmas. Don't ask me yet what that Thing is. Truth dwells in no man, but is a shy beast you must hunt as you may in the forests that are round about the Walls of Heaven. And I do hereby curse, gibbet, and denounce *in execrationem perpetuam atque aeternam* the

man who hunts in a crafty or calculating way
— as, lying low, nosing for scents, squinting
for trails, crawling noiselessly till he shall
come near to his quarry and then taking careful aim.   Here's to him who hunts Truth in
the honest fashion of men, which is, going
blindly at it, following his first scent (if such
there be) or (if none) none, scrambling over
boulders, fording torrents, winding his horn,
plunging into thickets, skipping, firing off his
gun in the air continually, and then ramming
in some more ammunition anyhow, with a
laugh and a curse if the charge explode in
his own jolly face.   The chances are he will
bring home in his bag nothing but a field-
mouse he trod on by accident.   Not the less
his is the true sport and the essential stuff of
holiness.

As touching Christmas — but there is
nothing like verse to clear the mind, heat the
blood, and make very humble the heart.
Rouse thee, Muse !

One Christmas Night in Pontgibaud
        (*Pom-pom, rub-a-dub-dub*)
A man with a drum went to and fro
        (*Two merry eyes, two cheeks chub*)

Nor not a citril within, without,
But heard the racket and heard the rout
And marvelled what it was all about
    (*And who shall shrive Beelzebub?*)

He whacked so hard the drum was split
    (*Pom-pom, rub-a-dub-dum*)
Out lept Saint Gabriel from it
    (*Praeclarissimus Omnium*)
Who spread his wings and up he went
Nor ever paused in his ascent
Till he had reached the firmament
    (*Benedicamus Dominum*).

That's what I shall sing (please God) at
dawn to-morrow, standing on the high, green
barrow at Storrington, where the bones of
Athelstan's men are.   **Yea,**

At dawn to-morrow
  On Storrington Barrow
I'll beg or borrow
  A bow and arrow
And shoot sleek sorrow
  Through the marrow.
The floods are out and the ford is narrow,
The stars hang dead and my limbs are
    lead,

But ale is gold
And there's good foot-hold
On the Cuckfield side of Storrington
    Barrow.

This too I shall sing, and other songs that
are yet to write. In Pagham I shall sing
them again, and again in Little Dewstead.
In Hornside I shall rewrite them, and at the
Scythe and Turtle in Liphook (if I have
patience) annotate them. At Selsey they will
be very damnably in the way, and I don't at
all know what I shall do with them at Selsey.

Such then, as I see it, is the whole pith,
mystery, outer form, common acceptation,
purpose, usage usual, meaning and inner
meaning, beauty intrinsic and extrinsic, and
right character of Christmas Feast. *Habent
urbs atque orbis revelationem.* Pray for my
soul.

A STRAIGHT TALK

By

G**RGE B*RN*RD SH*W

A STRAIGHT TALK

(Preface to "Snt George. A Christmas Play.")

WHEN a public man lays his hand on his heart and declares that his conduct needs no apology, the audience hastens to put up its umbrellas against the particularly severe downpour of apologies in store for it. I wont give the customary warning. My conduct shrieks aloud for apology, and you are in for a thorough drenching.

Flatly, I stole this play. The one valid excuse for the theft would be mental starvation. That excuse I shant plead. I could have made a dozen better plays than this out of my own head. You dont suppose Shakespeare was so vacant in the upper storey that there was nothing for it but to rummage through cinquecento romances, Townley Mysteries, and suchlike insanitary rubbish-heaps, in order that he might fish out enough scraps for his artistic fangs to fasten on. Depend on it, there were plenty of decent original notions seething behind yon marble brow. Why didn't our William use them? He was too lazy. And so am I. It is easier to give a new twist to somebody else's story that you take readymade than to perform that highly-specialised form of skilled labor which consists in giving artistic coherence to a story that you have conceived roughly for yourself. A literary gentleman once hoisted a theory that there are only thirty-six possible stories in the world. This—I say it with no deference at all—is bosh. There are as many possible stories in the world as there are microbes in the well-lined shelves of a literary gentleman's "den." On the other hand, it is perfectly true that only a baker's dozen of these have got themselves told. The reason lies in that bland, unalterable resolve to shirk honest work, by which you recognise the artist as surely as you recognise the leopard by his spots. In so far as I am an artist, I am a loafer. And if you expect me, in that line, to do anything but loaf, you will get the shock your romantic folly deserves. The only difference between me and my rivals past and present is that I have the decency to be ashamed of myself. So that if you are not too bemused and bedevilled by my "brilliancy" to kick me downstairs, you may rely on me to cheerfully lend a foot in the operation. But, while I have my share of judicial vindictiveness against crime, Im not going to talk the common judicial cant about brutality making a Better Man of the criminal. I havent the slightest doubt that I would thieve again at the earliest opportunity. Meanwhile be so good as to listen to the evidence on the present charge.

In the December after I was first cast ashore at Holyhead, I had to go down to Dorsetshire. In those days the more enterprising farm-laborers used still to annually dress themselves up in order to tickle the gentry into disbursing the money needed to supplement a local-minimum wage. They called themselves the Christmas Mummers, and performed a play entitled Snt George. As my education had been of the typical Irish kind, and the ideas on which I had been nourished were precisely the ideas that once in Tara's Hall were regarded as dangerous novelties, Snt George staggered me with the sense of being suddenly bumped up against a thing which lay centuries ahead of the time I had been born into. (Being, in point of fact, only a matter of five hundred years old, it would have the same effect to-day on the average London playgoer if it was produced in a west end theatre.) The plot was simple. It is set forth in Thomas Hardy's "Return of the Native"; but, as the people who read my books have no energy left over to cope with other authors, I must supply an outline of it myself.

Entered, first of all, the English Knight, announcing his determination to fight and vanquish the Turkish Knight, a vastly superior swordsman, who promptly made mincemeat of him. After the Saracen had celebrated his victory in verse, and proclaimed himself the world's champion, entered Snt George, who, after some preliminary patriotic flourishes, promptly made mincemeat of the Saracen — to the blank amazement of an audience which included several retired army officers. Snt George, however, saved his face by the usual expedient of the victorious British general, attributing to Providence a result which by no polite stretch of casuistry could have been traced to the operations of his own brain.

But here the dramatist was confronted by another difficulty : there being no curtain to ring down, how were the two corpses to be got gracefully rid of ? Entered therefore the Physician, and brought them both to life. (Any one objecting to this scene on the score of romantic improbability is hereby referred to the Royal College of Physicians, or to the directors of any accredited medical journal, who will hail with delight this opportunity of proving once and for all that re-vitalisation is the child's-play of the Faculty.)

Such then is the play that I have stolen. For all the many pleasing esthetic qualities you will find in it — dramatic inventiveness, humor and pathos, eloquence, elfin glamor and the like — you must bless the original author : of these things I have only the usufruct. To me the play owes nothing but the stiffening of civistic conscience that has been crammed in. Modest ? Not a bit of it. It is my civistic conscience that makes a man of me and (incidentally) makes this play a masterpiece.

Nothing could have been easier for me (if I were some one else) than to perform my task in that God-rest-you-merry-gentlemen-may-nothing-you-dismay spirit which so grossly flatters the sensibilities of the average citizen by its assumption that he is sharp enough to be dismayed by what stares him in the face. Charles Dickens had lucid intervals in which he was vaguely conscious of the abuses around him; but his spasmodic efforts to expose these brought him into contact with realities so agonising to his highstrung literary nerves that he invariably sank back into debauches of unsocial optimism. Even the Swan of Avon had his glimpses of the havoc of displacement wrought by Elizabethan romanticism in the social machine which had been working with tolerable smoothness under the prosaic guidance of Henry 8. The time was out of joint; and the Swan, recognising that he was the last person to ever set it right, consoled himself by offering the world a soothing doctrine of despair. Not for me, thank you, that Swansdown pillow. I refuse as flatly to fuddle myself in the shop of "W. Shakespeare, Druggist," as to stimulate myself with the juicy joints of "C. Dickens, Family Butcher." Of these and suchlike pernicious establishments my patronage consists in weaving round the shopdoor a barbed-wire entanglement of dialectic and then training my moral machine-guns on the customers.

In this devilish function I have, as you know, acquired by practice a tremendous technical skill; and but for the more or less innocent pride I take in showing off my accomplishment to all and sundry, I doubt whether even my iron nerves would be proof against the horrors that have impelled me to thus perfect myself. In my nonage I believed humanity could be reformed if only it were intelligently preached at for a sufficiently long period. This first fine careless rapture I could no more recapture, at my age, than I could recapture hoopingcough or nettlerash. One by one, I have flung all political nostra overboard, till there remain only dynamite and scientific breeding. My touching faith in these saves me from pessimism: I believe in the future; but this only makes the present — which I foresee as going strong for a couple of million of years or so — all the more excruciating by contrast.

For casting into dramatic form a compendium of my indictments of the present from a purely political standpoint, the old play of Snt George occurred to me as having exactly the framework I needed. In the person of the Turkish Knight I could embody that howling chaos which does duty among us for a body-politic. The English Knight would accordingly be the Liberal Party, whose efforts (whenever it is in favor with the electorate) to reduce chaos to order by emulating in foreign politics the blackguardism of a Metternich or Bismarck, and in home politics the spirited attitudinisings of a Garibaldi or Cavor, are foredoomed to the failure which its inherent oldmaidishness must always win for the Liberal Party in all undertakings whatsoever. Snt George is, of course, myself. But here my very aptitude in controversy tripped me up as playwright. Owing to my nack of going straight to the root of the matter in hand and substituting, before you can say Jack Robinson, a truth for every fallacy and a natural law for every convention, the scene of Snt George (Bernard Shaw)'s victory over the Turkish Knight came out too short for theatrical purposes. I calculated that the play as it stood would not occupy more than five hours in performance. I therefore departed from the original scheme so far as to provide the Turkish Knight with three attendant monsters, severally named the Good, the Beyootiful, and the Ter-rew, and representing in themselves the current forms of Religion, Art, and Science. These three Snt George successively challenges, tackles, and flattens out—the first as lunacy, the second as harlotry, the third as witchcraft. But even so the play would not be long enough had I not padded a good deal of buffoonery into the scene where the five corpses are brought back to life.

The restorative Physician symbolises that irresistible force of human stupidity by which the rottenest and basest institutions are enabled to thrive in the teeth of the logic that has demolished them. Thus, for the author, the close of the play is essentially tragic. But what is death to him is fun to you, and my buffooneries wont offend any of you. Bah !

FOND HEARTS ASKEW
By
M**R*CE H*WL*TT

FOND HEARTS ASKEW

To

WILLIAM ROBERTSON NICOLL
SAGE AND REVEREND
AND A TRUE KNIGHT
THIS ROMAUNT
OF DAYS EDVARDIAN

PROLOGUE.

TOO strong a wine, belike, for some stomachs, for there's honey in it, and a dibbet of gore, with other condiments. Yet Mistress Clio (with whom, some say, Mistress Thalia, that sweet hoyden) brewed it : she, not I, who do but hand the cup round by her warrant and good favour. Her guests, not mine, you shall take it or leave it — spill it untasted or quaff a bellyful. Of a hospitable temper, she whose page I am; but a great lady, over self-sure to be dudgeoned by wry faces in the refectory. As for the little sister (if she did have finger in the concoction) — no fear of offence there! I dare vow, who know somewhat the fashion of her, she will but trill a pretty titter or so at your qualms.

[169]

I cry you mercy for a lacuna at the outset. I know not what had knitted and blackened the brows of certain two speeding eastward through London, enhansomed, on the night of the feast of St. Box : *alter,* Geoffrey Dizzard, called "The Honourable," *lieu-tenant* in the Guards of Edward the Peace Getter ; *altera,* the Lady Angelica Plantagenet, to him affianced. Devil take the cause of the bicker : enough that they were at sulks. Here's for a sight of the girl !

Johannes Sargent, that swift giant from the New World, had already flung her on canvas, with a brace of sisters. She outstands there, a virgin poplar-tall ; hair like ravelled flax and coiffed in the fashion of the period ; neck like a giraffe's ; lips shaped for kissing rather than smiling ; eyes like a giraffe's again ; breasts like a boy's, and something of a dressed-up boy in the total aspect of her. She has arms a trifle long even for such height as hers ; fingers very long, too, with red-pink nails trimmed to a point. She looks out slantwise, conscious of her beauty, and perhaps of certain other things. Fire under

that ice, I conjecture — red corpuscles ramp-
ant behind that meek white mask of hers.
*"Forsitan in hoc anno pulcherrima debutan-
tium"* is the verdict of a contemporary journal. For *"forsitan"* read *"certe."* No slur,
that, on the rest of the bevy.

Very much as Johannes had seen her did
she appear now to the cits, as the cabriolet
swung past them. Paramount there, she was
still more paramount here. Yet this Geoffrey
was not ill-looking. In the secret journal of
Mary Jane, serving-wench in the palace of
Geoffrey's father (who gat his barony by
beer) note is made of his "lovely blue eyes ;
complexion like a blush rose ; hands like a
girl's ; lips like a girl's again ; yellow curls
close cropped ; and for moustachio (so young
is he yet) such a shadow as amber might cast
on water."

Here, had I my will, I would limn you
Mary Jane herself, that parched nymph.
Time urges, though. The cabrioleteer
thrashes his horse (me with it) to a canter,
and plunges into Soho. Some wagon
athwart the path gives pause. Angelica,
looking about her, bites lip. For this is the
street of Wardour, wherein (say all the

chronicles most absolutely) she and Geoffrey had first met and plit their troth.

"Methinks," cries she, loud and clear to the wagoner, and pointing finger at Geoffrey, "the Devil must be between your shafts, to make a mock of me in this conjunction, the which is truly of his own doing."

"Sweet madam," says Geoffrey (who was also called "The Ready"), "shall I help harness you at his side? Though, for my part, I doubt 'twere supererogant, in that he buckled you to his service or ever the priest dipped you."

A bitter jest, this; and the thought of it still tingled on the girl's cheek and clawed her heart when Geoffrey handed her down at the portico of Drury Lane Theatre. A new pantomime was afoot. Geoffrey's father (that bluff red baron) had chartered a box, was already there with his lady and others.

Lily among peonies, Angelica sat brooding, her eyes fastened on the stage, Geoffrey behind her chair, brooding by the same token. Presto, he saw a flood of pink rush up her shoulders to her ears. The "principal boy" had just skipped on to the stage. No boy at all (God be witness), but one Mistress Tina

Vandeleur, very apt in masquerado, and seeming true boy enough to the guileless. Stout of leg, light-footed, with a tricksy plume to his cap, and the swagger of one who would beard the Saints for a wager, this Aladdin was just such a galliard as Angelica had often fondled in her dreams. He lept straight into the closet of her heart, and "Deus!" she cried, "maugre my maidenhood, I will follow those pretty heels round the earth!"

Cried Geoffrey "Yea! and will not I presently string his ham to save your panting?"

"*Tacete!*" cried the groundlings.

A moment after, Geoffrey forgot his spleen. Cupid had noosed him — bound him tight to the Widow Twankey. This was a woman most unlike to Angelica: poplar-tall, I grant you; but elm-wide into the bargain; deep-voiced, robustious, and puffed bravely out with hot vital essences. Seemed so to Geoffrey, at least, who had no smattering of theatres and knew not his cynosure to be none other than Master Willie Joffers, prime buffo of the day. Like Angelica, he had had fond visions; and lo here, the very lady of them!

[173]

Says he to Angelica, "I am heartset on this widow."

"By so much the better!" she laughs. "I to my peacock, you to your peahen, with a God-speed from each to other."

How to snare the birds? A pretty problem: the fowling was like to be delicate. So hale a strutter as Aladdin could not lack for bonamies. "Will he deign me?" wondered meek Angelica. "This widow," thought Geoffrey, "is belike no widow at all, but a modest wife with a yea for no man but her lord." Head to head they took counsel, cudgelled their wits for some proper vantage. Of a sudden, Geoffrey clapped hand to thigh. Student of Boccaccio, Heveletius, and other sages, he had the clue in his palm. A whisper from him, a nod from Angelica, and the twain withdrew from the box into the corridor without.

There, back to back, they disrobed swiftly, each tossing to other every garment as it was doffed. Then a flurried toilet, and a difficult, for the man especially; but hotness of desire breeds dexterity. When they turned and faced each other, Angelica was such a boy as

Aladdin would not spurn as page, Geoffrey such a girl as the widow might well covet as body-maid.

Out they hied under the stars, and sought way to the postern whereby the mummers would come when their work were done. Thereat they stationed themselves in shadow. A bitter night, with a lather of snow on the cobbles; but they were heedless of that: love and their dancing hearts warmed them.

They waited long. Strings of muffled figures began to file out, but never an one like to Aladdin or the Widow. Midnight tolled. Had these two had wind of the ambuscado and crept out by another door? Nay, patience!

At last! A figure showed in the doorway—a figure cloaked womanly, but topped with face of Aladdin. Trousered Angelica, with a cry, darted forth from the shadow. To Mistress Vandeleur's eyes she was as truly man as was Mistress Vandeleur to hers. Thus confronted, Mistress Vandeleur shrank back, blushing hot.

"Nay!" laughs Angelica, clipping her by the wrists. "Cold boy, you shall not so

[175]

easily slip me. A pretty girl you make, Aladdin; but love pierces such disguise as a rapier might pierce lard."

"Madman! Unhandle me!" screams the actress.

"No madman I, as well you know," answers Angelica, "but a maid whom spurned love may yet madden. Kiss me on the lips!"

While they struggle, another figure fills the postern, and in an instant Angelica is torn aside by Master Willie Joffers (well versed, for all his mumming, in matters of chivalry). "Kisses for such coward lips?" cries he. "Nay, but a swinge to silence them!" and would have struck trousered Angelica full on the mouth. But décolleté Geoffrey Dizzard, crying at him "Sweet termagant, think not to baffle me by these airs of manhood!" had sprung in the way and on his own nose received the blow.

He staggered and, spurting blood, fell. Up go the buffo's hands, and "Now may the Saints whip me," cries he, "for a tapster of girl's blood!" and fled into the night, howling like a dog. Mistress Vandeleur had fled already. Down on her knees goes Angelica, to stanch Geoffrey's flux.

Thus far, straight history. Apocrypha, all the rest: you shall pick your own sequel. As for instance, some say Geoffrey bled to the death, whereby stepped Master Joffers to the scaffold, and Angelica (the Vandeleur too, like as not) to a nunnery. Others have it he lived, thanks to nurse Angelica, who, thereon wed, suckled him twin Dizzards in due season. Joffers, they say, had wife already, else would have wed the Vandeleur, for sake of symmetry.

DICKENS

By

G**RGE M**RE

DICKENS

I HAD often wondered why when people talked to me of Tintoretto I always found myself thinking of Turgéneff. It seemed to me strange that I should think of Turgéneff instead of thinking of Tintoretto; for at first sight nothing can be more far apart than the Slav mind and the Flemish. But one morning, some years ago, while I was musing by my fireplace in Victoria Street, Dolmetsch came to see me. He had a soiled roll of music under his left arm. I said, "How are you?" He said, "I am well. And you?" I said, "I, too, am well. What is that, my dear Dolmetsch, that you carry under your left arm?" He answered, "It is a Mass by Palestrina." "Will you read me the score?" I asked. I was afraid he would say no. But Dolmetsch is not one of those men who say no, and he read me the score. He did not read very well, but I had never heard it before, so when he finished I begged of him he would read it to me again. He said,

"Very well, M**re, I will read it to you again." I remember his exact words, because they seemed to me at the time to be the sort of thing that only Dolmetsch could have said. It was a foggy morning in Victoria Street, and while Dolmetsch read again the first few bars, I thought how Renoir would have loved to paint in such an atmosphere the tops of the plane trees that flaccidly show above the wall of Buckingham Palace. . . . Why had I never been invited to Buckingham Palace? I did not want to go there, but it would have been nice to have been asked. . . . How *brave gaillard* was Renoir, and how well he painted from that subfusc palette! . . .

My roving thoughts were caught back to the divine score which Arnold Dolmetsch was reading to me. How well placed they were, those semibreves! Could anyone but Palestrina have placed them so nicely? I wondered what girl Palestrina was courting when he conceived them. She must have been blonde, surely, and with narrow flanks. . . . There are moments when one does not think of girls, are there not, dear reader? And I swear to you that such a moment came to me while Dolmetsch mumbled the last two bars of that Mass. The notes were "do, la, sol, do, fa, do, sol, la," and as he mumbled them I sat upright and stared into space, for it had become suddenly plain to me why when people talked of Tintoretto I always found myself thinking of Turgéneff.

I do not say that this story that I have told to you is a very good story, and I am afraid that I have not well told it. Some day, when I have time, I should like to re-write it. But meantime I let it stand, because without it you could not receive what is upmost in my thoughts, and which I wish you to share with me. Without it, what I am yearning to say might seem to you a hard saying; but now you will understand me.

There never was a writer except Dickens. Perhaps you have never heard say of him? No matter, till a few days past he was only a name to me. I remember that when I was a young man in Paris, I read a praise of him in some journal; but in those days I was kneeling at other altars, I was scrubbing other doorsteps. . . . So has it been ever since; always a false god, always the wrong doorstep. I am sick of the smell of the incense I

have swung to this and that false god — Zola,
Yeats, *et tous ces autres*. I am angry to have
got housemaid's knee, because I got it on
doorsteps that led to nowhere. There is but
one doorstep worth scrubbing. The doorstep
of Charles Dickens. . . .

Did he write many books ? I know not,
it does not greatly matter, he wrote the
"Pickwick Papers"; that suffices. I have read
as yet but one chapter, describing a Christmas
party in a country house. Strange that anyone should have essayed to write about anything but that ! Christmas — I see it now
— is the only moment in which men and
women are really alive, are really worth
writing about. At other seasons they do not
exist for the purpose of art. I spit on all
seasons except Christmas. . . Is he not in all
fiction the greatest figure, this Mr. Wardell,
this old "squire" rosy-cheeked, who enter-
tains this Christmas party at his house ? He
is more truthful, he is more significant, than
any figure in Balzac. He is better than all
Balzac's figures rolled into one. . . I used to
kneel on that doorstep. Balzac wrote many
books. But now it behoves me to ask myself whether he ever wrote a good book.

One knows that he used to write for fifteen hours at a stretch, gulping down coffee all the while. But it does not follow that the coffee was good, nor does it follow that what he wrote was good. The Comédie Humaine is all chicory. . . I had wished for some years to say this, I am glad *d'avoir débarrassé ma poitrine de ça.*

To have described divinely a Christmas party is something, but it is not everything. The disengaging of the erotic motive is everything, is the only touchstone. If while that is being done we are soothed into a trance, a nebulous delirium of the nerves, then we know the novelist to be a supreme novelist. If we retain consciousness, he is not supreme, and to be less than supreme in art is to not exist. . . Dickens disengages the erotic motive through two figures, Mr. Winkle, a sportman, and Miss Arabella, "a young lady with fur-topped boots." They go skating, he helps her over a stile. Can one not well see her ? She steps over the stile and her shin defines itself through her balbriggan stocking. She is a knock-kneed girl, and she looks at Mr. Winkle with that sensual regard that sometimes comes when the wind is north-west. Yes, it is a north-west wind that is blowing over this landscape that Hals or Winchoven might have painted — no, Winchoven would have fumbled it with rose-madder, but Hals would have done it well. Hals would have approved — would he not ? — the pollard aspens, these pollard aspens deciduous and wistful, which the rime makes glistening. That field, how well ploughed it is, and are they not like petticoats, those clouds low-hanging ? Yes, Hals would have stated them well, but only Manet could have stated the slope of the thighs of the girl — how does she call herself ? — Arabella — it is a so hard name to remember — as she steps across the stile. Manet would have found pleasure in her cheeks also. They are a little chapped with the north-west wind that makes the pollard aspens to quiver. How adorable a thing it is, a girl's nose that the north-west wind renders red ! We may tire of it sometimes, because we sometimes tire of all things, but Winkle does not know this. Is Arabella his mistress ? If she is not, she has been, or at any rate she will be. How full she is of temperament, is she not ?

Her shoulder-blades seem a little carelessly modelled, but how good they are in intention ! How well placed that smut on her left cheek !

Strange thoughts of her surge up vaguely in me as I watch her — thoughts that I cannot express in English. . . Elle est plus vieille que les roches entre lesquelles ell s'est assise ; comme le vampire elle a été fréquemment morte, et a appris les secrets du tombeau ; et s'est plongée dans des mers profondes, et conserve autour d'elle leur jour ruiné ; et, comme Lède, était mère d'Hélène de Troie, et, comme Sainte-Anne, mère de Maria ; et tout cela n'a été pour elle que. . . . I desist, for not through French can be expressed the thoughts that surge in me. French is a stale language. So are all the European languages, one can say in them nothing fresh. . . . The stalest of them all is Erse. . . .

Deep down in my heart a sudden voice whispers me that there is only one land wherein art may reveal herself once more. Of what avail to await her anywhere else than in Mexico ? Only there can the apocalypse happen. I will take a ticket for

Mexico, I will buy a Mexican grammar, I will be a Mexican. . . . On a hillside, or beside some grey pool, gazing out across those plains poor and arid, I will await the first pale showings of the new dawn. . . .

EUPHEMIA
CLASHTHOUGHT
AN IMITATION OF
MEREDITH

EUPHEMIA CLASHTHOUGHT [1]

IN the heart of insular Cosmos, remote by some scores of leagues of Hodge-trod arable or pastoral, not more than a snuff-pinch for gaping tourist nostrils accustomed to inhalation of prairie winds, but enough for perspective, from those marginal sands, trident-scraped, we are to fancy, by a helmeted Dame Abstract familiarly profiled on discs of current bronze — price of a loaf for humbler maws disdainful of Gallic side-dishes for the titillation of choicer palates — stands Clashthought Park, a house of some pretension, mentioned at Runnymede, with the spreading exception of wings given to it in later times by Daedalean masters not to be baulked of billiards or traps for Terpsichore, and

[1] It were not, as a general rule, well to republish after a man's death the skit you made of his work while he lived. Meredith, however, was so transcendent that such skits must ever be harmless, and so lasting will his fame be that they can never lose what freshness they may have had at first. So I have put this thing in with the others, making improvements that were needed.—M. B.

owned for unbroken generations by a healthy line of procreant Clashthoughts, to the undoing of collateral branches eager for the birth of a female. Passengers through cushioned space, flying top-speed or dallying with obscure stations not alighted at apparently, have had it pointed out to them as beheld dimly for a privileged instant before they sink back behind crackling barrier of instructive paper with a "Thank you, Sir," or "Madam," as the case may be. Guide-books praise it. I conceive they shall be studied for a cock-shy of rainbow epithets slashed in at the target of Landed Gentry, premonitorily. The tintinnabulation's enough. Periodical footings of Clashthoughts into Mayfair or the Tyrol, signalled by the slide from its mast of a crested index of Aeolian caprice, blazon of their presence, give the curious a right to spin through the halls and galleries under a cackle of housekeeper guideship — scramble for a chuck of the dainties, dog fashion. There is something to be said for the rope's twist. Wisdom skips.

It is recorded that the goblins of this same Lady Wisdom were all agog one Christmas morning between the doors of the house and the village church, which crouches on the outskirt of the park, with something of a lodge in its look, you might say, more than of celestial twinkles, even with Christmas hoar-frost bleaching the grey of it in sunlight, as one sees imaged on seasonable missives for amity in the trays marked "sixpence and upwards," here and there, on the counters of barter.

Be sure these goblins made obeisance to Sir Peter Clashthought, as he passed by, starched beacon of squirearchy, wife on arm, sons to heel. After him, certain members of the household — rose-chapped males and females, bearing books of worship. The pack of goblins glance up the drive with nudging elbows and whisperings of "Where is daughter Euphemia? Where Sir Rebus, her affianced?"

Off they scamper for a peep through the windows of the house. They throng the sill of the library, ears acock and eyelids twittering admiration of a prospect. Euphemia was in view of them — essence of her. Sir Rebus was at her side. Nothing slips the goblins.

"Nymph in the Heavy Dragoons" was Mrs. Cryptic-Sparkler's famous definition of

her. The County took it for final — an uncut
gem with a fleck in the heart of it. Euphemia condoned the imagery. She had
breadth. Heels that spread ample curves
over the ground she stood on, and hands that
might floor you with a clench of them, were
hers. Grey eyes looked out lucid and fearless under swelling temples that were lost
in a ruffling copse of hair. Her nose was
virginal, with hints of the Iron Duke at most
angles. Square chin, cleft centrally, gave her
throat the look of a tower with a gun pro-
trudent at top. She was dressed for church
evidently, but seemed no slave to Time.
Her bonnet was pushed well back from her
head, and she was fingering the ribbons.
One saw she was a woman. She inspired
deference.

"Forefinger for Shepherd's Crook" was
what Mrs. Cryptic-Sparkler had said of Sir
Rebus. It shall stand at that.

"You have Prayer Book?" he queried.

She nodded. Juno catches the connubial
trick.

"Hymns?"

"Ancient and Modern."

"I may share with you?"

"I know by heart. Parrots sing."

"Philomel carols," he bent to her.

"Complaints spoil a festival."

He waved hand to the door. "Lady, your father has started."

"He knows the adage. Copy-books instil it."

"Inexorable truth in it."

"We may dodge the scythe."

"To be choked with the sands?"

She flashed a smile. "I would not," he said, "that my Euphemia were late for the Absolution."

She cast eyes to the carpet. He caught them at the rebound.

"It snows," she murmured, swimming to the window.

"A flake, no more. The season claims it."

"I have thin boots."

"Another pair?"

"My maid buttons. She is at church."

"My fingers?"

"Ten on each."

"Five," he corrected.

"Buttons."

"I beg your pardon."

She saw opportunity. She swam to the

bell-rope and grasped it for a tinkle. The action spread feminine curves to her lover's eyes. He was a man.

Obsequiousness loomed in the doorway. Its mistress flashed an order for port—two glasses. Sir Rebus sprang a pair of eyebrows on her. Suspicion slid down the banisters of his mind, trailing a blue ribbon. Inebriates were one of his hobbies. For an instant she was sunset.

"Medicinal," she murmured.

"Forgive me, Madam. A glass, certainly. 'Twill warm us for worshipping."

The wine appeared, seemed to blink owlishly through the facets of its decanter, like some hoary captive dragged forth into light after years of subterraneous darkness — something querulous in the sudden liberation of it. Or say that it gleamed benignant from its tray, steady-borne by the hands of reverence, as one has seen Infallibility pass with uplifting of jewelled fingers through genuflexions to the Balcony. Port has this in it : that it compels obeisance, master of us ; as opposed to brother and sister wines wooing us with a coy flush in the gold of them to a cursory tope or harlequin leap shimmering up the veins with a sly wink at us through eyelets. Hussy vintages swim to a cosset. We go to Port, mark you!

Sir Rebus sipped with an affectionate twirl of thumb at the glass's stem. He said "One scents the cobwebs."

"Catches in them," Euphemia flung at him.

"I take you. Bacchus laughs in the web."

"Unspun but for Pallas."

"A lady's jealousy."

"Forethought, rather."

"Brewed in the paternal pate. Grant it!"

"For a spring in accoutrements."

Sir Rebus inclined gravely. Port precludes prolongment of the riposte.

She replenished glasses. Depreciation yielded. "A step," she said, "and we are in time for the First Lesson."

"This," he agreed, "is a wine."

"There are blasphemies in posture. One should sit to it."

"Perhaps." He sank to commodious throne of leather indicated by her finger.

Again she filled for him. "This time, no heel-taps," she was imperative. "The Litany demands basis."

"True." He drained, not repelling the decanter placed at his elbow.

"It is a wine," he presently repeated with a rolling tongue over it.

"Laid down by my great-grandfather. Cloistral."

"Strange," he said, examining the stopper, "no date. Antediluvian. Sound, though."

He drew out his note-book. *"The senses,"* he wrote, *"are internecine. They shall have learned esprit de corps before they enslave us."* This was one of his happiest flings to general from particular. *"Visual distraction cries havoc to ultimate delicacy of palate"* would but have pinned us a butterfly best a-hover; nor even so should we have had truth of why the aphorist, closing note-book and nestling back of head against that of chair, closed eyes also.

As by some such law as lurks in meteorological toy for our guidance in climes close-knit with Irony for bewilderment, making egress of old woman synchronise inevitably with old man's ingress, or the other way about, the force that closed the aphorist's eye-lids parted his lips in degree according. Thus had Euphemia, erect on hearth-rug, a cavern to gaze down into. Outworks of tortifying ivory cast but denser shadows into the inexplorable. The solitudes here grew murmurous. To and fro through secret passages in the recesses leading up deviously to lesser twin caverns of nose above, the gnomes Morphean went about their business, whispering at first, but presently bold to wind horns in unison — Rolandwise, not less.

Euphemia had an ear for it; whim also to construe lord and master relaxed but reboant and soaring above the verbal to harmonic truths of abstract or transcendental, to be hummed subsequently by privileged female audience of one bent on a hook-or-crook plucking out of pith for salvation.

She caught tablets pendent at her girdle. *"How long,"* queried her stilus, *"has our sex had humour? Jael hammered."*

She might have hitched speculation further. But Mother Earth, white-mantled, called to her.

Casting eye of caution at recumbence, she paddled across the carpet and anon swam out over the snow.

Pagan young womanhood, six foot of it, spanned eight miles before luncheon.

[199]